THE ✹ TIMES
TOP 100
GRADUATE EMPLOYERS

The definitive guide to the leading employers recruiting graduates during 2008-2009.

HIGH FLIERS

HIGH FLIERS PUBLICATIONS LTD
IN ASSOCIATION WITH THE TIMES

Published by High Fliers Publications Limited
King's Gate, 1 Bravingtons Walk, London N1 9AE
Telephone: 020 7428 9100   Web: www.Top100GraduateEmployers.com

Editor Martin Birchall
Publisher Gill Thomas
Production Manager Robin Burrows
Portrait Photography Sarah Merson

The Times Top 100 Graduate Employers is based on research results from The UK Graduate Careers Survey 2008, produced by High Fliers Research Ltd.

Printed and bound in Italy by L.E.G.O. S.p.A.

A CIP catalogue record for this book
is available from the British Library.
ISBN 978-0-9536991-9-3

Contents

Information Request Service
Find out more about Britain's top employers and you could
win a Nintendo DS Lite or start your career £5,000 richer!

Foreword

by Martin Birchall
Editor, The Times Top 100 Graduate Employers

Welcome to the latest edition of *The Times Top 100 Graduate Employers*, your guide to the UK's leading employers who are recruiting graduates in 2008-2009. If you're one of the 320,000 final year university students due to graduate in the summer of 2009, then the employment outlook is still encouraging.

The good news is that the employers featured within the *Top 100* hired record numbers of graduates in 2007-2008 and are set to recruit similar numbers this year. Since 2004, Britain's most popular organisations have stepped up their entry-level positions for new graduates by more than 50 per cent and vacancies in some career sectors have more than doubled.

The less encouraging message is that after twelve months of the global 'credit crunch', chaos in the financial markets and the ensuing doom and gloom in the UK economy, the graduate job market's five-year unbroken run of growth – 10 to 12 per cent annually – has now come to an abrupt end. Employers expect to hire 1 per cent fewer new recruits during the 2008-2009 recruitment season and in several sectors the number of vacancies have been cut significantly.

Perhaps inevitably, there will be less graduate positions in investment banking in 2009 – the losses sustained by the best-known City banks since the start of the financial crisis are estimated to be at least $150 billion and there have been tens of thousands of redundancies in the sector during the last year.

It is worth remembering, though, that despite all the negative newspaper headlines, at least 600 major employers in the UK currently operate a recognised graduate recruitment scheme. For most of these, hiring new graduates is about developing a steady supply of future managers and leaders for their organisation, rather than simply filling immediate job vacancies. Few employers will be keen to break this talent pipeline and so – irrespective of the worsening economic conditions – most are expecting to maintain their graduate recruitment, albeit with some reductions in vacancy numbers.

There are also literally hundreds of small and medium-sized businesses that rely on hiring ambitious new graduates for their organisations, often recruiting direct from local universities.

Given that there continues to be a wide choice of different types of employment and graduate jobs, how can prospective employers be assessed and ranked?

To find out, we interviewed over 15,000 final year students who graduated from universities across the UK in the summer of 2008, and asked them "Which employer do you think offers the best opportunities for graduates?". Between them, the 'Class of 2008' named organisations from every imaginable employment sector and business type – from the 'Big Four' accounting &

professional services firms to manufacturers, investment banks to government departments, leading charities to well-known IT companies and consulting firms. The one hundred employers who were mentioned most often during the research form *The Times Top 100 Graduate Employers*.

This book is therefore a celebration of the employers who are judged to offer the brightest prospects for graduates. Whether by the perceived quality of their training programmes, the business success that they enjoy, the scale of their organisations, or by the impression that

their recruitment promotions have made – these are the employers that are most attractive to university-leavers in 2009.

The Times Top 100 Graduate Employers will not necessarily identify which organisation is right for you: only you can decide that. But it is an invaluable reference if you want to discover what Britain's leading employers have to offer.

Leaving university and finding your first job can be a daunting process but it is one of the most important steps you'll ever take. Having a good understanding of the range of opportunities available must be the best way to start.

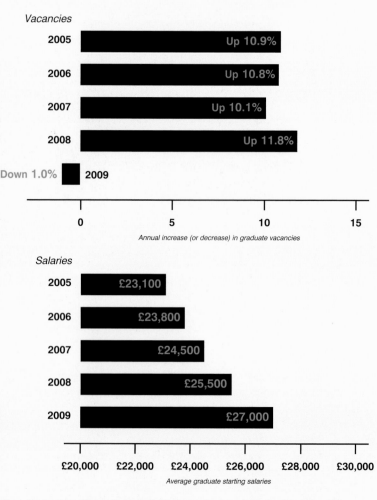

THE TIMES
TOP 100
GRADUATE EMPLOYERS

How Graduate Vacancies and Starting Salaries have Changed 2005-2009

Vacancies

2005	Up 10.9%
2006	Up 10.8%
2007	Up 10.1%
2008	Up 11.8%
2009	Down 1.0%

Annual increase (or decrease) in graduate vacancies

0   5   10   15

Salaries

2005	£23,100
2006	£23,800
2007	£24,500
2008	£25,500
2009	£27,000

£20,000 £22,000 £24,000 £26,000 £28,000 £30,000

Average graduate starting salaries

Source **The Times Top 100 Graduate Employers 2005-9**, High Fliers Research Ltd. Annual change in graduate vacancy levels and average starting salaries in 2005-2009 at the organisations featured in The Times Top 100 Graduate Employers

We make sure the cream always rises to the top

When a dairy farmer wants cream, they'll make sure the herd gets through 50kg of feed and 100 litres of water a day each. We make sure our graduates get a salary of £40k and a fully expensed Audi A4. But we just want the cream – not the herd. The Aldi Graduate Area Manager Training Programme takes the best and makes them better. And it's in this unique environment that you will be able to gain real responsibility and enjoy tangible career progression at a rate unknown in other companies. So yes, the benefits are there for all to see. But they won't be offered around to all and sundry. It will be your unflinching commitment and will to succeed that will mark you out as the type of person we're looking for. But then, if you are aiming for the top, what better place than in a global business that's in the Top 10 of 'The Times Top 100 Graduate Employers'? Find out more on page 72. **aldi.co.uk/recruitment**

Graduate
Area Manager
£40,000

rising to
£57,750
after three years

Fully expensed
Audi A4

Opportunity
for directorship
within 5 years

International
secondment
opportunities

Berlin's rich history.
Regular cross-border contact.

Start thinking European.

Graduate Programmes – All Degree Disciplines

From the moment you join a KPMG Graduate Programme, you'll need to think European. That's because the recent merger between our UK, German, Swiss and Spanish firms has allowed us to offer you something that virtually none of our competitors can – wide exposure to international clients and a unique, engaging opportunity to experience business the length and breadth of Europe. So, whether you choose to specialise in Audit, Tax or Advisory, one thing's for certain. You'll have the strength, scope and success of Europe's largest fully integrated accountancy firm to inspire and challenge you.

Visit www.kpmg.co.uk/careers to find out more and apply.

AUDIT ▪ TAX ▪ ADVISORY

KPMG

Compiling the Top 100 Graduate Employers

by Gill Thomas
Publisher, High Fliers Publications Ltd

The growth in graduate vacancies at Britain's best-known organisations may have stalled this year, but the total number of entry-level positions for university-leavers has risen by over 50 per cent since 2004 and an estimated five thousand organisations will still be competing to hire the best graduates from UK universities during the 2008-2009 recruitment season.

With such a wide choice of employment, selecting the organisation that is 'right' for you can be quite a challenge. How can you evaluate the different opportunities and decide which employers offer the best career paths? What basis can you use to assess so many possible training programmes and graduate positions?

It's clear there are no simple answers to these questions and no single individual employer can ever hope to be right for every graduate – everyone makes their own judgements about the organisations they want to work for and the type of job they find the most attractive.

How then can anyone produce a meaningful league table of Britain's leading graduate employers? What criteria can define whether one organisation is 'better' than another? To compile *The Times Top 100 Graduate Employers*, the independent market research company, High Fliers Research Ltd, interviewed 15,381 final year students who left UK universities in the summer of 2008. These students from the 'Class of 2008' who took part in the study were selected at random to represent the full cross-section of finalists at their universities, not just those who had already secured graduate employment. The research examined students' experiences during their search for a graduate job and asked them about their attitudes to employers.

The key question used to produce the *Top 100* was "Which employer do you think offers the best opportunities for graduates?" This question was deliberately open-ended and students were not prompted in any way. Across the whole survey, finalists mentioned more than 600 different organisations – from the smallest local employers, to some of the world's best-known companies. The responses were analysed to identify the number of times each employer was mentioned. The one hundred organisations that were mentioned most often are the *The Times Top 100 Graduate Employers* for 2008.

Looking at the considerable selection of answers given by finalists from the 'Class of 2008' it's clear that individual students used very different criteria to determine which employer they considered offered the best opportunities for graduates. Some focused on employers' general reputations – their public image, their business profile or their commercial success. Others evaluated employers based on the information they had seen during their job search – the quality of recruitment promotions, the impression formed from meeting employers' representatives,

THE TIMES
TOP 100
GRADUATE EMPLOYERS

The Top 100 Graduate Employers 2008

This Year	Last Year		This Year	Last Year	
1.	1	PricewaterhouseCoopers	51.	46	Barclays Capital
2.	2	Deloitte	52.	70	Royal Navy
3.	3	KPMG	53.	56	Bloomberg
4.	7	Accenture	54.	49	Lloyds TSB
5.	6	NHS	55.	69	HBOS
6.	4	Civil Service	56.	59	Lehman Brothers
7.	5	BBC	57.	58	Slaughter and May
8.	9	Aldi	58.	63	ExxonMobil
9.	14	Teach First	59.	66	Bain & Company
10.	10	Goldman Sachs	60.	75	Boots
11.	11	Ernst & Young	61.	100	The Co-operative Group
12.	8	HSBC	62.	53	Oxfam
13.	15	Procter & Gamble	63.	55	Freshfields Bruckhaus Deringer
14.	13	GlaxoSmithKline	64.	52	Eversheds
15.	18	Army	65.	78	British Airways
16.	12	Shell	66.	77	GCHQ
17.	17	Marks & Spencer	67.	47	Arcadia Group
18.	16	Royal Bank of Scotland Group	68.	85	Herbert Smith
19.	19	BP	69.	43	Atkins
20.	26	Tesco	70.	71	Credit Suisse
21.	33	Morgan Stanley	71.	84	Boston Consulting Group
22.	22	J.P. Morgan	72.	93	DLA Piper
23.	21	IBM	73.	64	Lovells
24.	39	Google	74.	79	McDonald's Restaurants
25.	24	Rolls-Royce	75.	92	Bank of America
26.	45	Clifford Chance	76.	NEW	Sky
27.	30	L'Oréal	77.	62	Pfizer
28.	25	Police	78.	NEW	Innocent Smoothies
29.	31	Allen & Overy	79.	90	Faber Maunsell
30.	32	Citi	80.	NEW	Oliver Wyman
31.	34	Microsoft	81.	NEW	E.ON
32.	27	Barclays Bank	82.	61	ASDA
33.	23	Unilever	83.	80	Fujitsu
34.	48	Cancer Research UK	84.	86	Penguin
35.	20	UBS	85.	91	Addleshaw Goddard
36.	41	BAE Systems	86.	NEW	Airbus
37.	42	BT	87.	65	Thomson Reuters
38.	29	Deutsche Bank	88.	72	Corus
39.	38	Mars	89.	89	Transport for London
40.	28	Linklaters	90.	NEW	QinetiQ
41.	36	Merrill Lynch	91.	NEW	Watson Wyatt
42.	35	RAF	92.	NEW	The Met Office
43.	44	AstraZeneca	93.	96	MI5 – The Security Service
44.	57	Arup	94.	NEW	Ministry of Defence
45.	51	Foreign Office	95.	67	Cadbury
46.	60	WPP	96.	87	npower
47.	54	John Lewis	97.	NEW	Grant Thornton
48.	37	McKinsey & Company	98.	NEW	Data Connection
49.	40	Local Government	99.	NEW	CMS Cameron McKenna
50.	50	Sainsbury's	100.	NEW	BNP Paribas

Source **The UK Graduate Careers Survey 2008**, High Fliers Research Ltd. 15,381 final year students leaving UK universities in the summer of 2008 were asked 'Which employer do you think offers the best opportunities for graduates?'

or experiences through the recruitment and selection process. FInalists also considered the level of vacancies that organisations were recruiting for as an indicator of possible employment prospects, or were influenced by employers' profile on campus.

Many final year students, however, used the 'employment proposition' as their main guide – the quality of graduate training and development an employer offers, the salary & remuneration package available, and the practical aspects of a first job such as location or working hours.

Irrespective of the criteria that students used to arrive at their answer, the hardest part for many was just selecting a single organisation. To some extent, choosing two or three, or even half a dozen employers would have been much easier. But the whole purpose of the exercise was to replicate the reality that everyone faces – you can only work for one organisation. And at each stage of the job search there are choices to be made as to which direction to take and which employers to pursue.

The resulting *Top 100* is a dynamic league table of the UK's most exciting and well-respected graduate recruiters in 2008. This year's race to be number one in *The Times Top 100 Graduate Employers* has been the closest since the league table was first published in 1997 – with just 7 votes separating the top two employers. But, by this narrowest of margins, the accounting & professional services firm PricewaterhouseCoopers has held onto the top spot and is confirmed the UK's top graduate recruiter for the fifth year running, with a total of 8.2 per cent of finalists' votes.

The firm's arch-rivals Deloitte achieved a noticeably higher profile on-campus during the 2008 recruitment round and increased its share of the *Top 100* vote by a quarter year-on-year but finished in second place for the third consecutive year, a tantalising 0.1 per cent behind PwC. KPMG was unchanged at number three for the third time, despite also increasing its share of the student vote this year.

Accenture, the consulting and technology company, has moved up three places to 4th place, its best ranking since 2004 and the NHS has joined the top five for the first time. Both the Civil Service and the BBC have slipped two places each but budget retailer Aldi has risen

again, this time to 8th place. The hugely successful Teach First scheme has climbed another five places to 9th position, continuing its rapid rise up the rankings since entering the *Top 100* in 63rd place just five years ago. Banking group HSBC has dropped out of the top ten for the first time since 2002 and investment bank Goldman Sachs is ranked in 10th position for a third year.

Britain's most successful retailer, Tesco, has recorded a jump of six places to reach the top twenty for the first time, Procter & Gamble has moved up two places to 13th and the Army has reversed its downward trend of the last three years and is now ranked in 15th position. Ernst & Young, Marks & Spencer and BP are each unchanged in 11th, 17th and 19th places respectively and both the Royal Bank of Scotland Group and GlaxoSmithKline have edged lower.

The highest climbers in 2008 are led by The Co-operative Group which has leapt an impressive thirty-nine places to 61st and law firm DLA Piper which moves up twenty-one places to 72nd. Another well-known law firm, Clifford Chance, also fared well rising from 45th to 26th place this year. The Royal Navy also did well, climbing from 70th up to 52nd position.

The City's leading investment banks may have had a difficult time following the turmoil in the global financial markets but they remain the largest single group of employers in *The Times Top 100 Graduate Employers* and continue to be a very popular career destination for many final year students. UBS, Deutsche Bank, Barclays Capital and Merrill Lynch have each dropped down the *Top 100* rankings but J.P. Morgan is unchanged in 22nd place and the Bank of America, Morgan Stanley, Citi and Credit Suisse have all managed to improve their positions.

There are a total of thirteen new entries in this year's *Top 100*, the highest being for satellite television company Sky in 76th place. Innocent Smoothies, which recruits a decidedly modest five graduates annually, appears in 78th place just ahead of consulting firm Oliver Wyman and energy group E.ON. The Met Office joins the rankings for the first time in 92nd place and the consulting firm Watson Wyatt appears for the first time since 2003. Six organisations – Airbus, the defence employer QinetiQ, the Ministry of

Defence, accounting firm Grant Thornton and Data Connection, the Enfield-based IT company – have all returned to this year's *Top 100* after dropping out of the list in 2007.

Among the organisations leaving the *Top 100* in 2008 are the law firms Baker & McKenzie and Norton Rose, consulting firms Mercer and Capgemini, the Financial Services Authority, the investment bank ABN Amro, transport group Maersk, Saatchi & Saatchi, Diageo, Intel and the Environment Agency. Last year's highest new entries BDO Stoy Hayward and GE both also failed to retain their places.

This year's edition of *The Times Top 100 Graduate Employers* has produced a number of significant changes, particularly towards the top of the list, and the results provide a unique insight into how graduates from the 'Class of 2008' rated the leading employers. The majority of these organisations are featured in the 'Employer Entry' section of this book. Starting on page 63, you can see a two-page profile for each employer, listed alphabetically for easy reference.

The editorial part of the entry includes a short description of what the organisation does, its opportunities for graduates and its recruitment programme for 2008-2009. A fact file for each employer gives details of the number of graduate vacancies, the business functions that graduates are recruited for, likely starting salaries for 2009, application deadlines, the universities that the employer is intending to visit during the year, and contact details for their recruitment website and graduate brochure. The right-hand page of the entry contains a display advert from the employer.

If you would like to find out more about any of the employers featured in *The Times Top 100 Graduate Employers*, then you can use the book's 'Information Request Service' – simply register your personal details and the employers you are interested in using the request card that appears opposite page 256, or go online to **www.Top100GraduateEmployers.com** – the new website showcasing the latest news and information about *Top 100* organisations.

You'll receive email bulletins about the employers, details of their presentations and careers events at your university, and other information about their graduate recruitment. The service is entirely free and you choose which organisations you would like to hear about.

Using the 'Information Request Service' enters you into a prize draw to win **£5,000**. There are also 50 **Nintendo DS Lites** to be won – one at each of the universities at which *The Times Top 100 Graduate Employers* book is distributed – for those who return information request cards before **30th November 2008**.

THE ✦✦✦ TIMES
TOP 100
GRADUATE EMPLOYERS

Employers in this year's Top 100

		Number of Employers			Number of Employers
1.	Investment Bank	12	9.	Consulting Firm	6
2.	Law Firm	11	10.	Bank or Financial Institution	5
3.	Public Sector Employer	11	11.	Oil or Energy Company	5
4.	Retailer	10	12.	Accountancy or Professional Services Firm	5
5.	Engineering or Industrial Company	8	13.	Armed Forces	3
6.	IT or Telecoms Company	6	14.	Chemical or Pharmaceutical Company	3
7.	Fast-Moving Consumer Goods Company	6	15.	Charity or Voluntary Sector	2
8.	Media Company	6	16.	Other	1

Source **The UK Graduate Careers Survey 2008**, High Fliers Research Ltd. 15,381 final year students leaving UK universities in the summer 2008 were asked 'Which employer do you think offers the best opportunities for graduates?'

Assurance
Tax
Advisory
Actuarial
Consulting

Requirements:
2:1 in any subject
280 UCAS tariff
or equivalent

Nationwide Opportunities Spring and Autumn 2009

Three cheers. We've just been named **number one in The Times Top 100 Graduate Employers survey for the fifth year running**. And we'd like to thank everyone who voted. Our continuing popularity may be down to the sheer variety of our work, projects and clients. Or perhaps it's the fact we offer early client exposure. Then again, it could be because graduates can specialise in a specific business area or choose to experience a number of areas, picking up valuable technical, business and personal skills as they go. Chances are though, it's all of the above. And we hope it's enough to attract you. Aim for the top. There's only one number one employer – so find out why we're the one firm for all talented graduates.

pwc.com/uk/careers/

Text: PwC to 85792
(Texts charged at your standard network rate.)

We value diversity in our people.

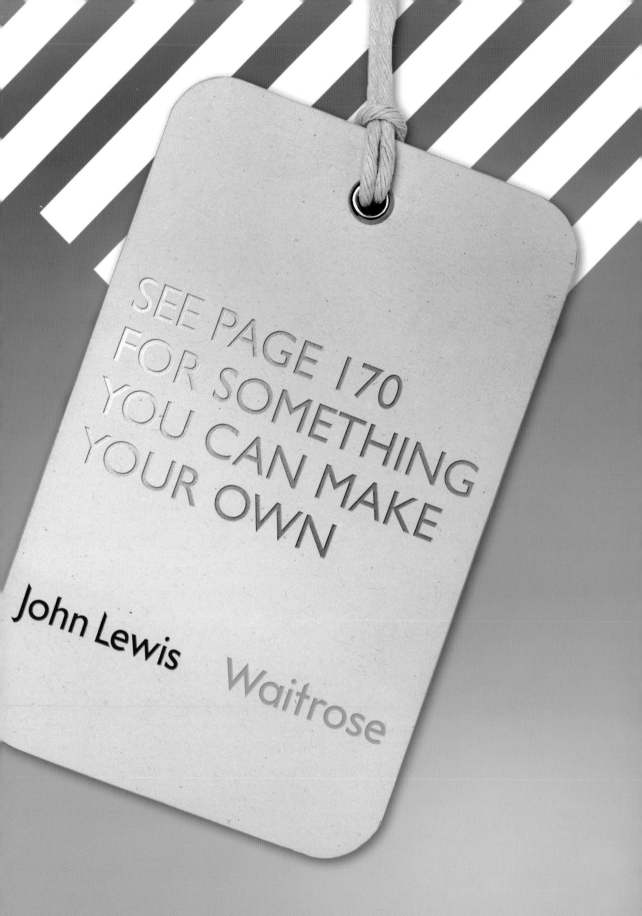

SEE PAGE 170
FOR SOMETHING
YOU CAN MAKE
YOUR OWN

John Lewis   Waitrose

John Lewis Partnership

The Times Graduate Recruitment Awards

As well as *The Times Top 100 Graduate Employers* league table, students from the 'Class of 2008' were also asked about the 'graduate employers of choice' within individual career sectors.

Finalists who were actively applying for graduate jobs in sixteen separate areas, such as engineering, IT, finance, human resources, sales and marketing etc, were asked the open-ended question 'Which employer would you most like to work for?'.

The winners of *The Times Graduate Recruitment Awards 2008* are listed here:

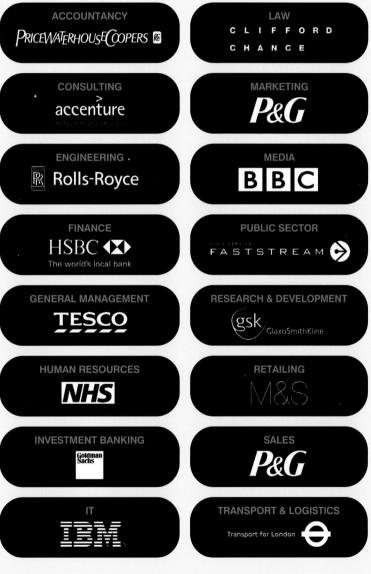

Source **The UK Graduate Careers Survey 2008**, High Fliers Research Ltd. 15,381 final year students leaving university in the summer 2008 were asked 'Which employer do you most want to work for?' within the career sectors they had applied to.

THE TIMES
TOP 100
GRADUATE EMPLOYERS

How to use the directory

Many of the employers listed within The Times Top 100 Graduate Employers are featured in the 'Employer Entries' section of the directory. These entries describe what each organisation does, the opportunities they offer graduates, and practical details about their recruitment programme for 2008-2009.

The 'Employer Entry' section begins on page 63.

Each entry follows a standard format, and contains two elements: descriptive text and easy-to-find information on the employer's vacancies, contact details and salary expectations.

Locations of jobs
The regional locations of the employer's jobs are highlighted in red.

Vacancies
The number of likely graduate vacancies at this employer in 2008-2009

Career areas recruited for
Details of the generic career areas that the employer recruits into. There are 17 areas to look out for:

- Accountancy
- Consulting
- Engineering
- Finance
- General Management
- Human Resources
- Investment Banking
- IT
- Law
- Logistics
- Manufacturing
- Marketing
- Media
- Purchasing
- Research & Development
- Retailing
- Sales

Employer's graduate recruitment website

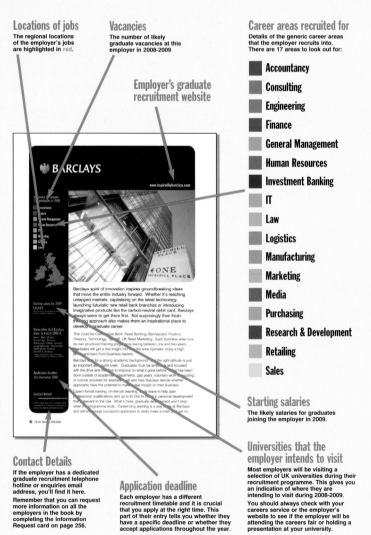

Starting salaries
The likely salaries for graduates joining the employer in 2009.

Universities that the employer intends to visit
Most employers will be visiting a selection of UK universities during their recruitment programme. This gives you an indication of where they are intending to visit during 2008-2009.
You should always check with your careers service or the employer's website to see if the employer will be attending the careers fair or holding a presentation at your university.

Contact Details
If the employer has a dedicated graduate recruitment telephone hotline or enquiries email address, you'll find it here.
Remember that you can request more information on all the employers in the book by completing the Information Request card on page 256.

Application deadline
Each employer has a different recruitment timetable and it is crucial that you apply at the right time. This part of their entry tells you whether they have a specific deadline or whether they accept applications throughout the year.

Who makes sure the
loudest bands
get the green light?

From rock to reggae, metal to mod, Wembley Stadium has been home to some of the biggest bands in history. So, when we were asked to provide the power for the famous arch, we needed to make sure we were completely in tune with the planet. The solution was a unique renewable energy contract that ensures we match our normal supply with electricity provided by our own windfarms on the coast. Meaning that even when some of the bands' lyrics are a little blue, we can honestly say we stay green.

It's this sort of thinking that our graduates face every day. And why we're looking for talented, bright people to join us in engineering, general business management, finance, business analysis, risk or IS within RWE IT UK (not the snappiest lyrics in the world we agree, but we had to tell you what careers are on offer).

If you fancy blowing your own trumpet, visit www.brightergraduates.com to find out more.

RWE Group

Graduate opportunities, all disciplines.

If you want a career that offers more of the things that really count, welcome to AstraZeneca. We turn good ideas into effective medicines and our innovation enhances the lives of patients around the world.

If you're a graduate with serious talent and big ambitions, you'll never be just another face in the crowd. Our approach to development is focused on giving you the support you need to reach your potential – and rewarding your performance as an individual.

I want
to be
recognised

Find the recognition you deserve at
ideas.astrazeneca.com
sign up for job alerts and let the opportunities come to you

AstraZeneca
life inspiring ideas

Understanding the Graduate Market

by Carol Lewis
Careers Editor, The Times

Over the last five years, the graduate job market has boomed. Vacancies for university-leavers at the UK's most popular employers have grown by between 10 and 12 per cent annually and every major employment sector has increased its graduate recruitment.

In the period from 2003 to 2008, the number of trainee positions in accountancy went up by over 80 per cent, City investment banks doubled their intake, major retailers took on 40 per cent more graduates and Britain's industrial giants stepped up their recruiting by a third. A thriving economy meant new graduates had the best choice of employment for nearly two decades.

But in little more than 12 months, the economic outlook has been thrown into chaos. The global 'credit crunch', rising inflation and interest rates, sky-high fuel prices and the continued turbulence in world financial markets have taken their toll on business and consumer confidence.

With this backdrop, it was perhaps inevitable that the UK's leading employers would be more cautious about their future graduate recruitment. As a result, vacancies at *The Times Top 100 Graduate Employers* are set to dip by 1 per cent in 2009, the first drop in entry-level jobs since 2003. Together, the employers in this year's *Top 100* are advertising jobs for 19,956 graduates, compared to the 20,158 hired in 2008-2009.

Within different parts of the employment market, there is a very mixed picture. Vacancies at the top City banks are down by 13 per cent, accountancy firms have trimmed their targets by 3 per cent but recruitment numbers at consumer goods manufacturers and in the media have fallen by a third.

Elsewhere, employment prospects are brighter with extra graduate vacancies in IT & telecoms, engineering, retailing and the Armed Forces. And the public sector is planning to boost its recruitment by more than a fifth in the coming year, making it the fastest-growing graduate employer for 2009.

There are now an average of 120 vacancies per *Top 100* employer but a fifth of organisations plan to hire at least 250 new recruits and three employers anticipate hiring at least 1,000 university-leavers.

In all, a quarter of leading employers plan to hire more graduates this recruitment season than last, more than half believe they will recruit similar numbers to 2008, while a fifth expect to cut their total graduate intake.

The largest number of vacancies in 2009 are at accountancy firms (21.0 per cent of total graduate jobs) or investment banks (18.3 per cent of total). This is good news for those with a head for figures. But don't panic if you are an arts graduate – almost all the major professional services firms and financial institutions say they

With around 330,000 employees and 10,000 offices in 83 countries and territories, HSBC is one of the largest financial services organisations in the world, and one of the few banks with a truly global presence. We are recognised for combining this truly global reach with local knowledge, the wide range of products and services we offer, and the expertise of our people. HSBC provides a comprehensive range of financial services to over 125 million customers worldwide.

The size of the HSBC Group means that we are able to provide a wide range of financial services to our clients, both national and international. It also means that we can offer our people careers of unlimited potential.

Exceptional graduates of any discipline are recruited onto our world class training programmes, preparing them for management and executive positions across the business. These include Commercial Management, Executive Management, Insurance Broking, Information Technology, Retail Management, Marketing, HR, European Management, Trainee Financial Planning Management, Operations Management, International Management, Global Banking and Markets, Group Private Banking and Global Asset Management.

HSBC also offers a range of internships to promising undergraduates, both in their first year or penultimate year of study.

To find out more about the opportunities that HSBC can offer and to apply online, visit www.hsbc.com/studentcareers

HSBC
The world's local bank

are keen to recruit people from a broad range of degree backgrounds. They are not just looking to hire ready-made accountants and bankers.

According to a recent study by Dr Elizabeth Marx, a partner at headhunters Heidrick and Struggles, the majority of chief executives of UK FTSE100 companies come from a background of working in financial management. This suggests that many of today's graduate jobs really could be the first rung on the ladder to a stellar career.

The employers who plan to hire the fewest graduates in 2009 are in the chemical & pharmaceutical sector (0.3 per cent of total graduate jobs), consumer goods and the charity & voluntary sector (both 1.0 per cent).

The biggest individual graduate recruiters in *The Times Top 100 Graduate Employers* during 2008-2009 are PricewaterhouseCoopers (1,200 vacancies), Deloitte and KPMG (1,000 vacancies each), Ernst & Young (750 vacancies), the Army

and RAF (700 vacancies), the RBS Group and Deutsche Bank (600 vacancies), Accenture and the Civil Service Fast Stream (500 vacancies). The smallest recruiter is Innocent Smoothies – a new entry into this year's *Top 100* which hired just 5 graduates in 2008.

More than half of the *Top 100* companies have graduate vacancies in financial management and IT, two fifths have opportunities in human resources, a third offer jobs in marketing and engineering, a quarter of employers are hiring sales executives and a fifth are looking for research & development personnel.

Only ten of the *Top 100* employers have media vacancies, but the media continues to be one of the most desirable career destinations for graduates, this suggests that graduates intent on pursuing media careers would do well to consider applying to employers outside the *Top 100* or looking for vacancies that are not

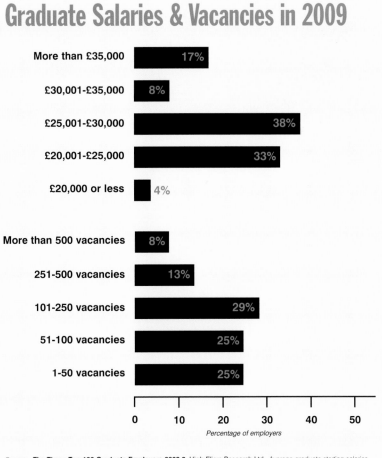

Graduate Salaries & Vacancies in 2009

	Percentage of employers
More than £35,000	17%
£30,001-£35,000	8%
£25,001-£30,000	38%
£20,001-£25,000	33%
£20,000 or less	4%
More than 500 vacancies	8%
251-500 vacancies	13%
101-250 vacancies	29%
51-100 vacancies	25%
1-50 vacancies	25%

Percentage of employers

Source **The Times Top 100 Graduate Employers 2008-9**, High Fliers Research Ltd. Average graduate starting salaries and total number of graduate vacancies in 2009 at the organisations featured in The Times Top 100 Graduate Employers.

specifically classified as graduate jobs.

Recent results from *The UK Graduate Careers Survey 2008* – a survey of more than 15,000 final year students conducted by High Fliers Research – showed that most wanted to work in London and the south of England. Let's hope the same is true in 2009 because four-fifths of leading employers are recruiting graduates to work in the capital and half had vacancies in the south east of England, the Midlands or the North West. By contrast, fewer than 50 per cent had any positions available in Scotland, Wales or Northern Ireland. The region with the fewest graduate employers is East Anglia.

Most people want an interesting and satisfying career but the fiscal reality is that with the average

student leaving university £12,000 in debt salaries do matter. Fortunately, despite the worsening economic outlook, the UK's leading graduate employers are boosting starting salaries by 5.9 per cent in 2009, taking average packages to £27,000 – a £1,500 increase on last year's average graduate starting salary.

More than a quarter of the top graduate programmes will now pay graduates at least £30,000 when they start work. The most generous salaries tend to be those on offer from investment banks (an average of £38,000), law firms (an average of £37,400), and consulting firms (an average of £31,000).

There is much more to life than money though and graduates really need to consider what

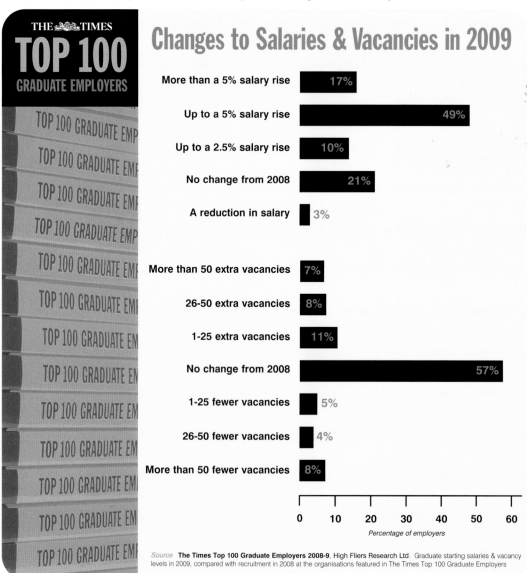

Changes to Salaries & Vacancies in 2009

	Percentage of employers
More than a 5% salary rise	17%
Up to a 5% salary rise	49%
Up to a 2.5% salary rise	10%
No change from 2008	21%
A reduction in salary	3%
More than 50 extra vacancies	7%
26-50 extra vacancies	8%
1-25 extra vacancies	11%
No change from 2008	57%
1-25 fewer vacancies	5%
26-50 fewer vacancies	4%
More than 50 fewer vacancies	8%

Percentage of employers

Source **The Times Top 100 Graduate Employers 2008-9**, High Fliers Research Ltd. Graduate starting salaries & vacancy levels in 2009, compared with recruitment in 2008 at the organisations featured in The Times Top 100 Graduate Employers

Wouldn't you
like to have it all?
Don't let anyone ever
tell you that you can't.

Choosing where to launch your career is one of the most important decisions
you'll ever make. So pick an organisation that offers you everything you deserve.
We mean early responsibility. Dynamic training opportunities. Career progression.
The chance to work successfully with a diverse range of clients in a collaborative
culture. And in a firm that values its people and gives back to society.

The more you discover about us, the more you'll discover about yourself.
So secure a place on our 2009 graduate programme now. Applications opened
early this year and places are limited. Look out for big things on campus.
It's your future. How far will you take it?

Discover more at **www.deloitte.co.uk/graduates**

motivates them, what career development and training opportunities are available, the work-life balance they want and their long-term career strategies. None of the *Top 100* employers which publish starting salary details are paying less than £19,000 to their new graduates.

Most of *The Times Top 100 Employers* are actively marketing their graduate vacancies at between 15 and 20 UK universities this year. Organisations use a variety of careers fairs, campus recruitment presentations and media advertising. The universities likely to host the most events run by Britain's leading graduate employers in 2008-2009 are Manchester, London, Warwick, Cambridge, Oxford, Bristol, Durham and Nottingham.

But if the company you'd most like to work for isn't visiting your university then don't despair, log on instead – every major employer has its own website which will give full details about their graduate recruitment programmes, often complete with case studies. What is more, most employers will accept work experience and graduate applications online.

Half of the UK's top employers now recruit all the year-round and will accept applications throughout the 2008-2009 recruitment season.

For employers with a single application deadline, the most common deadlines are in November or December, although law firms usually have July closing dates.

There are lots of reasons to feel positive about life after graduation. Despite this year's dip in vacancies the number of graduate positions for university-leavers at *Top 100* employers are still 50 per cent higher than in 2004 and starting salaries for new graduates have increased by an impressive 19 per cent over the same period.

Few people can expect to walk straight into a job – there is tough competition for all vacancies and the top employers have rigorous selection procedures which include multi-round tests and assessments. Graduates not only need to gain a good degree – most of the top employers want to recruit those with a first or 2.1 – but also pick up vital soft skills along the way. Employers crave well-rounded individuals with demonstrable competencies such as communication skills, motivation and organisation, the ability to work in teams and leadership potential.

But for those finalists who do make the grade, there continue to be many rewarding careers and some great starting salaries on offer at *The Times Top 100 Graduate Employers*.

THE TIMES TOP 100 GRADUATE EMPLOYERS

Graduate Employment in 2009, by Industry

2008			% of total vacancies in 2009	How graduate vacancies compare with 2008
1.	1	**Accountancy or Professional Services Firms**	21.0	Down 3.4%
2.	2	**Investment Banks or Fund Managers**	18.3	Down 13.1%
3.	3	**Public Sector**	10.5	Up 21.7%
4.	4	**Armed Forces**	9.5	Up 11.8%
5.	5	**Engineering or Industrial Companies**	8.0	Up 3.9%
6.	6	**Banking or Financial Services**	7.0	Up 5.7%
7.	7	**Retailers**	5.6	Up 3.2%
8.	8	**Law Firms**	5.3	Up 1.0%
9.	9	**Consulting Firms**	3.6	No change
10.	10	**IT & Telecommunications Companies**	3.6	Up 3.6%
11.	11	**Oil & Energy Companies**	3.1	Down 6.4%
12.	12	**Media Organisations**	1.7	Down 32.0%
13.	14	**Charity or Voluntary Organisations**	1.0	No change
14.	13	**Consumer Goods Manufacturers**	1.0	Down 31.3%
15.	14	**Chemical & Pharmaceuticals**	0.3	No change

Source **The Times Top 100 Graduate Employers 2008-9**, High Fliers Research Ltd. Graduate vacancy levels in 2009, compared with total numbers recruited in 2008 at the organisations featured in The Times Top 100 Graduate Employers

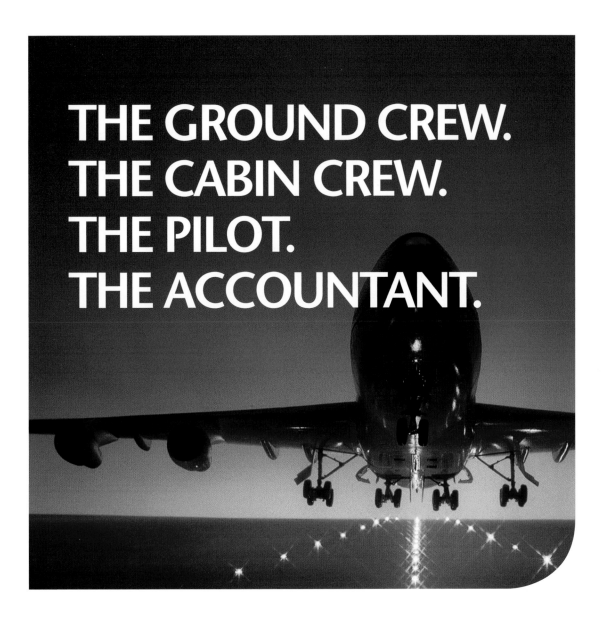

THE GROUND CREW.
THE CABIN CREW.
THE PILOT.
THE ACCOUNTANT.

A soaring success…

Have you got what it takes to secure your dream career? The ACA qualification from the ICAEW gives you access to so many amazing career opportunities, it prepares you for life as a business leader, pivotal to the success of any organisation. If you're looking for a career that will take off, look no further than the ACA.

To find out more:
E careers@icaew.com
www.icaew.com/careers

THE INSTITUTE
OF CHARTERED
ACCOUNTANTS
IN ENGLAND AND WALES

Make an imp
on your boss.

(And on their boss too).

official partner

ression

Graduate Leadership Programme
General Management / Finance / HR / Corporate Markets / IT / Retail Leaders

With a small and select graduate intake, your achievements will be recognised. That's why our Leadership Programme has been designed to ensure you thrive in the spotlight. Over the 2 year programme, you'll develop your judgement, influencing skills and ability to deliver on carefully selected assignments. Make no mistake. This is a challenging programme that will thoroughly test your drive and motivations. But with these qualities – and a good degree – we'll make sure you reach your full potential within one of the UK's largest and most successful financial services organisations. Find out more on our website.

lloydstsbjobs.co.uk/talent

 Lloyds TSB | for the journey...

 We value diversity and always appoint on merit.

Successful Job Hunting

by Dr Paul Redmond
Head of Careers & Employabilty Service, University of Liverpool

There's no 'right time' to begin thinking about your future or researching possible employment options, but the earlier you start, the easier the process can be. Increasing numbers of students are career-focused from their very first days at university, many others begin job hunting in their second year of studies, but some still leave things until their final year or even later.

Most UK universities have their own dedicated careers and employability service, so whenever you do choose to look into the graduate job market, help is at hand. Careers services provide a wealth of information about different occupations and employers as well as support and personal guidance during the application and selection process.

One of the first things you can do when visiting your careers service is to arrange to talk to a careers adviser. Although there is a huge volume of employment information on the internet, it's still really valuable to speak to someone who will listen to your ideas and interests and doesn't expect you to have a perfect plan worked out for the next forty years. You can usually see an adviser either on a 'drop-in' basis for a short consultation or by appointment for a longer session. In practice, you should be able to see an adviser very quickly, although at the busiest times of the year there may be a few days' wait for appointments.

The assistance that careers advisers can provide really depends on where you are up to in your job search. Some people are highly organised and already know more or less what it is they'd like to do – in which case an adviser can help put them in touch with specific recruiters or help them with their job applications.

Alternatively, you might be more of a 'window shopper' – considering three or four possible career areas. In this case, an adviser will encourage you to think through what each different option could involve and can point you towards relevant information or recruitment events.

If you're one of the many in the 'I just don't know what's out there' category and are starting out from scratch, then a tour of the careers service and its resources may be a very useful first step. Most services keep wide-ranging information on individual employers, occasionally supplemented with case studies, alumni notes and details of work experience opportunities. Careers service information staff are very skilled at explaining the many resources that are available such as careers publications, recruitment directories and employers' own literature.

You should also get to know your way round the careers service website – this will enable you to keep in touch with all the latest vacancies, details of campus events and online employer

OUT OF MULTIPLE OPTIONS, HOW DO YOU PICK THE BEST PERFORMER?

Our ability to judge performance, not just now, but for the long term, has underpinned our position as one of the world's leading investment banks. We have a strong and growing presence in emerging markets and we're one of only four banks worldwide to be AA+ rated by Standard and Poor's. But what can we invest in to secure our ongoing success?

The answer is simple – ideas and the people who have them. New ideas, new products, new markets – the financial world is continuously changing as markets emerge and technologies evolve. Your vision, commercial sense, and ability to tackle problems and contribute to your team could be critical in a world where ideas are currency and intellectual rigour is the difference between success and failure.

That's why, even in the face of difficult market conditions, we're still looking for people like you to make us even better.

Investing in ideas
graduates.bnpparibas.com

BNP PARIBAS
CORPORATE & INVESTMENT BANKING

files. The range of information is usually excellent and some websites include podcasts, video clips and blogs from recent graduates, as well as key labour market intelligence and networking resources.

So what are the key stages during the search for a graduate job? Make no mistake it can take a great deal of effort to land the role you want – you'll almost certainly need to work at it on an almost daily basis whilst you're researching your options, applying to employers and going through the selection process.

An important first step is to think about what type of work you might be suited to. This could include thinking about the experience you've had in the past with summer placements or part-time jobs and talking to other students, alumni, university tutors or members of your family to find out what working in different fields is really like. There are a whole series of questions that careers advisers can use to help you decide which issues are most important to you. Is it an organisation's culture or their geographical location or the graduate starting salaries that matter to you most?

Although having a good degree is invaluable, employers are also looking for graduates who can offer much more in the way of 'personal capital' – work experience, extracurricular achievements and positions of responsibility. This is what gives graduates a key advantage in the job market and certainly shouldn't be overlooked.

Employers take working with the Student Union, running key clubs and societies, or other similar student activities very seriously because they involve taking responsibility and can help develop your leadership skills or ability to work in a team. From this point of view, it's essential to make the most of your time at university. Graduate recruiters are much less interested in the so-called 'wash & go' students who've just come in for their lectures and then go off home again, because they haven't really engaged in university life.

Don't worry about coming up with the perfect job title – many of the jobs that today's graduates will do in their future careers haven't even been invented yet – just try and pinpoint the things that you like doing and interest you now. Thinking of your career as an open book will prepare you to

be flexible as the job market changes and evolves.

Once you do start to home in on particular areas that appeal to you, a great way to narrow the list of potential employers is to go along to campus recruitment events. Most careers services run introductory evenings on a particular employment area such as banking, IT or the media and many employers hold their own university presentations or take part in local careers fairs.

Company presentations tend to be quite formal and many employers approach them rather like a workshop or lecture with questions at the end. Careers fairs are generally more informal so it's your chance to go there and find out more about the organisations that are exhibiting. This isn't to suggest that you can relax – students do occasionally find that some of the people they meet on the stands turn out to be interviewers and selectors!

Over the last couple of years across the UK there has been an increase in parents attending careers fairs with students. It's an issue you need to think long and hard about – what kind of impression will it give to recruiters if your parents are there with you?

The key to getting the most out these events is being prepared. Your careers service will probably produce its own 'What's On' guide, which will give you a breakdown of those employers who will be visiting your university during the year. This will help you plan a timetable, while also ensuring that you don't miss out on crucial events. It's got to fit in around your own academic work and assignment but it's equally essential not to miss out on any of the key events.

When you do meet with an employer, it's important to manage the interaction and learn how to network effectively. Make sure you take each presentation or fair seriously and think through the questions that you'd like to ask employers in advance – don't be afraid to take a notepad and pencil with you. The staff employers send to campus to talk about their company have been hand-picked and they're there for a reason – they'll be great ambassadors for the organisation but often they'll also be recent graduates from your university, so it's quite alright to ask them how they got into the company and what tips they might be able to give you.

Having met with employers in person, you should have a much clearer idea about which organisations you'd like to apply to. Given that each individual application can take around eight hours to complete properly, it's not practical to try and fill in dozens. Plus, the closing dates can be very early in the autumn in certain sectors, such as banking and consulting, so you'll need to plan your approach and prioritise these applications carefully.

Of course, there is no magic total number of applications that will guarantee success, and if you apply to too many employers there is always the risk that you diminish the overall quality of your applications. Ideally, the organisations that you apply to should be ones that you are most committed to because this will shine through on your applications.

However, we do sometimes come across students who take a more strategic view of the application process, adopting more 'player-like' approaches. Whichever way you choose, your careers service can help you understand how competitive different sectors are – you may need to be realistic and weigh up the odds of finding work in the most popular areas.

Approach each application from scratch because, after all, each recruiter is looking for different skills, qualities and aptitudes. Graduate job applications generally consist of a mix of open and closed questions – some asking for specific factual information like your academic results and work experience record, with others asking for more discussion-based answers.

Remember, the reason that recruiters ask these questions is because they have a checklist of skills, qualities and experiences that they are looking for – you'll need to demonstrate that you match these requirements. Getting the right 'tone of voice' in application forms can be tricky – be positive, pleasantly assertive and confident and try to avoid saying things like "it was only" or "I just did".

Whether the application is online or a paper form, it's important to do a preliminary draft. Don't be afraid to bring it into the careers service

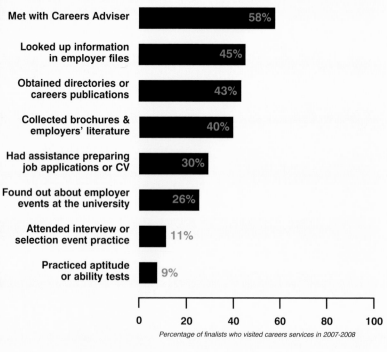

Careers Service Facilities used in 2007-8

Met with Careers Adviser	58%
Looked up information in employer files	45%
Obtained directories or careers publications	43%
Collected brochures & employers' literature	40%
Had assistance preparing job applications or CV	30%
Found out about employer events at the university	26%
Attended interview or selection event practice	11%
Practiced aptitude or ability tests	9%

0   20   40   60   80   100

Percentage of finalists who visited careers services in 2007-2008

Source **The UK Graduate Careers Survey 2008**, High Fliers Research Ltd. 15,381 final year students who left university in the summer of 2008 were asked about the facilities that they'd used at their local university careers service during 2007-2008.

From 93,000,000 miles away
to the energy in your home.

We're going there and beyond.

Careers in Engineering, Science & Business

Solar. Wind. Hydrogen. Natural gas. We have a ten-year plan
to invest more than $8 billion on clean, secure alternative
energy solutions, helping the world prepare for a low-
carbon future. Visit www.bpalternativeenergy.com
to see what we are doing to secure new energy for the
long term. This is the future; and it could be yours too.
Look beyond the limits.

BP is an equal opportunity employer.

bp

beyond petroleum·

www.bp.com/ukgraduates

and go through your answers and edit them with a careers adviser.

If your application is successful, the next stage is likely to be some form of interview with a recruiter to find out 'why do you want to work for us?' and 'what can you offer us?'. First interviews are sometimes held on campus or at a company office but are increasingly taking place by telephone.

The golden rule for these is to always wear a suit – by dressing as if you're going to meet your interviewer in person it helps get you into the right frame of mind. Some psychologists would even tell you to stand up as well, because you sound better and can breathe properly, but you should certainly banish friends, family and other distractions because they're always mysteriously drawn to you when you're doing a telephone interview.

Bear in mind that all interviews are assessments and are designed to test whether you match up to the application you've made. It may seem like a chat, but it's a chat with a very definite purpose. The recruiter will have your application form in front of them so it's vital you keep a copy of all the applications you make and re-read your submission before the interview. Think about the points you want to stress in the interview and plan the five key selling points that you want to get across.

In many organisations, the next stage is the assessment centre. These are often held over two days and include a battery of tests, exercises and group activities. Assessors will be observing how you interact with others, lead team exercises and maintain your levels of motivation. All in all, the experience can seem a bit like finding yourself on the TV programme, 'The Apprentice'.

Assessment centres generally include several types of test. Cognitive tests are designed to examine skills such as numeracy, literacy or the ability to think quickly, whilst personality-based tests explore what sort of person you are. Psychologists are still debating the extent to which you can practice these tests, but my advice would be to always try them out beforehand if you can. But don't worry. I've never yet encountered anyone who's failed a personality test!

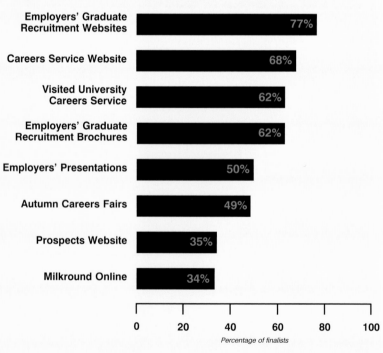

Recruitment Promotions used in 2007-8

Employers' Graduate Recruitment Websites	77%
Careers Service Website	68%
Visited University Careers Service	62%
Employers' Graduate Recruitment Brochures	62%
Employers' Presentations	50%
Autumn Careers Fairs	49%
Prospects Website	35%
Milkround Online	34%

0   20   40   60   80   100

Percentage of finalists

Source **The UK Graduate Careers Survey 2008**, High Fliers Research Ltd. 15,381 final year students who left university in the summer of 2008 were asked about the recruitment promotions that they'd used or taken part in during 2007-2008.

Many students tell us that the tests and group exercises often aren't the hardest aspect of assessment centres. The most daunting part of the experience is often the formal dinner and its accompanying small-talk with recruiters and managers.

There are a number of ways you can prepare for this – apart from practicing which cutlery to use with which course! Doing your homework about the organisation beforehand is always helpful, so that you've got something relevant to talk about. These 'casual' dinner conversations are often just as much a part of the selection process as the formal recruitment activities. Employers want graduates who can represent their businesses and their brands – people who can communicate well, put others at ease, and get by in different social occasions.

Assuming you survive this final selection experience, you may find yourself in the enviable position of having more than one job offer. Your last challenge, therefore, will be to decide which organisation to join.

At this stage, it's a question of looking very closely at what each employer is promising, not just in the short-term but over a longer period. Salary could be an important issue but also ask yourself 'where could I be in five years' time with this organisation?'. Think through 'what kind of training and development can I get?' and consider whether the geographical location of the jobs and the opportunities for travel fit in with your own plans. Don't feel under pressure to accept an offer too quickly – employers are usually quite happy to give you time to think things through.

If, despite all your applications and interviews, you don't manage to secure a job offer, keep your spirits up and stay motivated. The graduate job market remains highly competitive with at least 20 finalists chasing every vacancy, so you may not succeed straightaway. But just because things haven't worked out first time, it doesn't mean they won't next time. 'Plan B' is a case of saying 'let's re-visit the strategy, what was I trying to achieve, and why didn't I get the jobs I was looking for?'

It is well worth continuing to make applications right up until you graduate and beyond – many employers have different intakes during the year. Your careers service will be able to help you understand why things might have gone wrong and give you tips and guidance about how to improve your future applications. They may also recommend getting additional work experience to strengthen your CV or suggest you look into different career sectors.

Once you've graduated, if you need further help and advice, don't be afraid to stay in touch with your careers service – we are available for you to use for several years after you have completed your studies. And remember, even when you've landed your dream job, keep in touch with us and let us know what you're doing. Your experiences in the job market today can help serve as an inspiration to students tomorrow.

THE TIMES TOP 100 GRADUATE EMPLOYERS

Leading Destinations for 2008 Graduates

		% who wanted to work in sector			% who wanted to work in sector
1.	Media	13.1	11.	Human Resources	6.0
2.	Investment Banking	12.6	12.	Finance	5.5
3.	Teaching	12.4	13.	Sales	5.4
4.	Marketing	11.4	14.	General Management	5.2
5.	Accountancy	11.2	15.	Retailing	4.4
6.	Research & Development	10.9	16.	IT	3.5
7.	Consulting	10.8	17.	Armed Forces	3.0
8.	Charity or Voluntary Work	9.7	18.	Property	2.7
9.	Law	9.3	19.	Buying or Purchasing	2.6
10.	Engineering	7.3	20.	Police	2.4

Source **The UK Graduate Careers Survey 2008**, High Fliers Research Ltd. 15,381 final year students who left university in the summer of 2008 were asked which sectors they had applied to or planned to apply to for a graduate job.

CONTRACTING & PROCUREMENT
FINANCE
HUMAN RESOURCES
INFORMATION TECHNOLOGY
SALES & MARKETING
SUPPLY & DISTRIBUTION
TRADING

GEOLOGY/GEOPHYSICS
PETROPHYSICS
PRODUCTION TECHNOLOGY
PRODUCT/PROCESS RESEARCH
ENGINEERING:
RESERVOIR/PETROLEUM
WELL
PRODUCTION
PROCESS
ASSET MAINTENANCE
PROJECT/FACILITIES
DISCIPLINE

Respecting opinions. Sharing ideas. Improving communication. For Shell, these aren't just nice things to achieve, but vital elements in our bottom-line business strategy.

It's about acting as an integrated team and behaving in ways that benefit the business as a whole. Like everyone at Shell, you'll value different people's input and always consider how your actions impact on others.

We won't simply take your best ideas on board – we'll also help you explore them. Our personal development, skills training and culture of continuous learning are designed to give you all the tools you need to succeed.

So if you want to achieve more in your career, get together with Shell. Find out more at **www.shell.com/careers** and quote reference GAL311G when you apply.

Shell is an Equal Opportunity Employer.

www.shell.com/careers

See it
How far a career with Shell could take you

Achieving more together

Discover a world

where the only string attached

to freedom is responsibility.

As a private, family-owned business, we're in the driving seat when it comes to shaping
our future, and our success. With far fewer restrictions than most businesses, Mars
graduates get all the support, freedom and responsibility they need. But ultimately, it's
the graduates themselves that drive their projects forward. It's no surprise that so many
go on to achieve great things, both within Mars and throughout the business world.

Freedom takes courage. We take the courageous.   **MARS** incorporated   mars.com/ultimategrads

Making the Right Career Choices

by Simon Howard
'Job File' Columnist, The Sunday Times

f you're anything like me, you won't take kindly being told that 'this is the biggest decision you'll ever take'. After all, you were probably told that when you chose A levels, or degree course, or campus. But trust me, this really is the biggest choice you will ever make. Because (for all but the inherited aristocracy), what you do, and who you do it for, defines everything from here forward.

It defines where you live, who you meet, who you settle down with (people meet their partners at work more than anywhere else), how long you holiday, where you holiday, how long you work… perhaps even how many children you do or do not have. And yet it is one of the decisions "the system" least equips you to take.

The best bit of career advice I ever got at university was from my personal tutor. As I was pondering the options of post-graduate study (laughable), a career in the Prison Service (I'd have lasted a week) or continuing as doorman at a local nightclub (shortcut to a different sort of prison career), Dr ("hey, call me Bob") Dowse put me straight; "just get out there and earn some bloody money".

As it turns out, he was right, and although it took a while for me to accept it, I have to admit that deep down I am probably an entrepreneur (particularly as the company we founded seven years ago has now grown to 250 people with offices in three continents). But it didn't start out

like that, and to this day, I wish I'd understood my range of career options better – because although "Bob" was subsequently proved right, I had a pretty blinkered view of my options in that final year – and certainly could have got off to a better and faster start.

So let's start taking those blinkers off by understanding a little about the market for graduate skills: The big question for 2009 is whether we are going to see any big shocks in graduate recruitment. Well, there's no doubt that if you decide to head for a career straight from your Finals that you will be launching yourself into a tougher market. But that would be no bad thing. For a start, the recruiters themselves will be taking it all even more seriously – which will result in a pretty high level of commitment to those they do eventually offer jobs to. Second, it will do you no harm to start your career in harder times – as entrepreneurs like to think; "any fool can make money when the going's good".

If 2009 does turn out like previous years it is likely that the 'traditional' graduate recruiters (i.e. those with structured graduate training programmes) will only recruit something like 23,000 graduates. However, about 190,000 of the 2009 class will be in UK employment within twelve months of leaving university.

That is because the big truth is that the majority of graduates (roughly 167,000 by this count) will not join formal graduate programmes, but will

We want to be as diverse as the city we represent and welcome applications from everyone regardless of age, gender, ethnicity, sexual orientation, faith or disability.

We are the UK's first 24-hour, fully-staffed cycle park. We are one of the world's largest

Integrated Automatic Vehicle Location projects. We are £40billion of investment over

ten years. We are home to some of the world's first hydrogen buses. We are one

of the world's largest electronic ticketing projects. We are 20,000 employees.

We are 7 million customers. We are Transport for London. www.tfl.gov.uk/graduates

MAYOR OF LONDON Transport for London

find their way into junior roles with a wide range of employers. Not only can it be a great way to the top, but it reinforces the fact that far more important than the company you target, is the career that you choose.

Let me quote just one example which illustrates why understanding your options is so important: The idea of running a national newspaper may sound quite appealing – and rightly so. What's more, I know, or have known, eight people who have sat in the Managing Director's chair at places like the Times, Sun, Guardian et al. But not one of those eight people joined a graduate training programme.

In fact, they all started in trainee roles along with other people who certainly weren't graduates. However, in what job did they start in the media world? Which sector would you think that the future managing directors of national newspapers are drawn? You could make a good argument for marketing, and media would clearly be a strong contender but the correct answer is actually sales, currently one of the least popular of graduate destinations. That's because most of the senior managers in the newspaper and magazine world come from the commercial side, and the commercial side is dominated by sales, because filling pages with advertising is the absolute lifeblood of most publications.

So who'd have thought it? If you want to run Guardian Media Group, it's nothing to do with your political correctness, range of opinions or even journalistic ability, it's down to mean selling skills and absolute charm (believe me, I know her).

Many of last year's finalists did target careers in the commercial world, where competition is tough but the long term rewards are not just a very well paid career, but also a route to the very top. That is particularly true of areas like accountancy, investment banking, marketing and consulting. In almost complete contrast to those options are what I call 'vocational careers' – teaching, charity work, the Armed Forces and the police – where each sector offers within it a wide range of individual specialisms, but where commitment to that sector will tend to mean a career in itself.

One fascinating option – and arguably a key reason why teaching is an increasingly popular choice for graduates – is the innovative Teach First scheme. This offers new recruits the opportunity to teach for two years before starting a career in areas such as banking, law, consulting and

advertising. But Teach First is a rarity. Very seldom do you get the chance to switch careers without paying a penalty – and usually that penalty means starting all over again. Which is yet another reason for making the right choice at the outset.

Having watched the popularity of different career sectors and different employers over the years, it's always been interesting to see how preferences change. A decade ago consulting was the number one career choice whereas for the last three years jobs in the media have topped students' applications. Looking at the types of organisation, there has been a steady rise in the popularity of small and medium-sized firms. This is just as well, not only because they probably employ more graduates than any other sector, but they probably also offer faster progression – although that has to be balanced by typically less structured training.

But trends are only of passing interest, and you must decide which sector is right for you. If your heart is set on a career in investment banking ("heart" and investment banking are not always the easiest of bedfellows) then that's what you should aim for. However, you might have to accept that your way into an investment bank might not be through the front door, on a conventional graduate scheme – especially if 2009 is a tougher year for conventional schemes.

Unfortunately the biggest challenge every finalist faces is truly understanding what each sector offers. For example, fewer than one in fifty graduates applied for a position in either logistics or property in 2008. Now, I can tell you that logistics is one of the most intrinsically interesting areas of business. For the right person it's a rewarding, demanding career, just not that sexy.

On the other hand, property is probably one of the most entrepreneurial sectors and can reap some of the richest rewards. On a recent day at the races, the contrast between marketing (a top five destination for 2008 graduates) and property could not have been more stark. Ms Successful Marketeer was there in the box, dripping in Versace, oozing charm and sophistication, but sadly she spent most of the day on her mobile (that's a service business for you) and drank only water. Mr Property on the other hand had just completed a big deal and was Mr Relaxed for the day. His PA called once – she said everyone who had called could wait until the next day – his horse won the third race and he left in a helicopter.

Okay, these are extreme examples but each sector is very different, especially in the salary levels, type of work, environment and training they offer – and it's not always that apparent from the outside.

Throughout this year you will be bombarded with all sorts of careers messages about how wonderful a career in this or that might be, and how xyz company is so socially responsible, loving and caring, you'll wonder how they've never been nominated for a Nobel prize or at the very least been put up for canonization.

Your challenge is to see through that fog and think about what you're good at, what you're interested in and what you want to get out of a career. You can then start matching all that to what is a huge range of career choices. Going into the City because that's what your mates all want to do, is not a good enough reason.

You need to do your homework on career sectors, because if that results in you making the right career choice, it will be the best investment you'll ever make.

Simon Howard is a founder of Work Group plc. His book "Creating a Successful CV" is published by Dorling Kindersley, price £4.99.

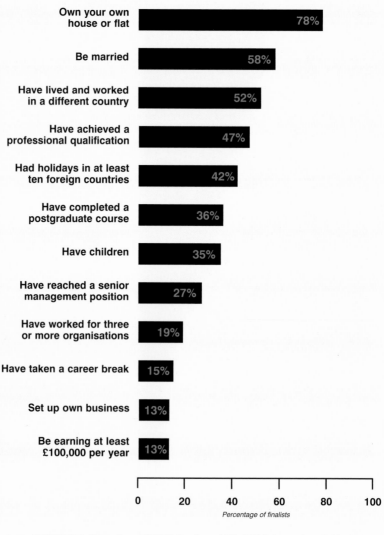

What the 'Class of 2008' Expect by Age 30

Own your own house or flat	78%
Be married	58%
Have lived and worked in a different country	52%
Have achieved a professional qualification	47%
Had holidays in at least ten foreign countries	42%
Have completed a postgraduate course	36%
Have children	35%
Have reached a senior management position	27%
Have worked for three or more organisations	19%
Have taken a career break	15%
Set up own business	13%
Be earning at least £100,000 per year	13%

Percentage of finalists

Source **The UK Graduate Careers Survey 2008**, High Fliers Research Ltd. 15,381 final year students who left university in the summer of 2008 were asked 'What do you think you'll have done by the age of 30?'.

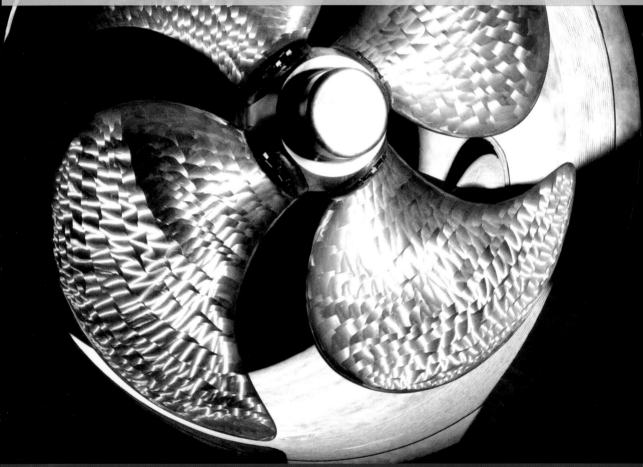

"Today I powered a different kind of thinking."
What will you do tomorrow?

Engineering · Finance · Supply Chain · Purchasing · Operations Management · HR · Commercial · Customer Management · Marketing · Project Management

Graduate opportunities

It's no wonder our graduates are proud to work for us. From developing aircraft engines that produce lower emissions, ship engines that run on liquefied gas and compression systems that move 12 million m³ of gas an hour, to negotiating with major suppliers and customers, they contribute to a variety of exciting projects that power the world we live in.

Join us and you'll discover that we're leading the way in the civil and defence aerospace, energy and marine sectors. Whether you want to develop your professional expertise or your leadership ability, our graduate programmes are designed to meet your needs in a variety of business areas. So, what will you do tomorrow? To find out more about the opportunities on offer, just visit www.rolls-royce.com/university

Trusted to deliver excellence

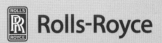

The Power of interaction.

Interactivity can be an art form. Just ask The JD Project, our forward-thinking new media client. Their fresh take on Internet TV won them an International Emmy™ Award. The namecheck they gave us in their acceptance speech showed that our approach to commercial law gets results. Now we want new trainee solicitors to help us interact with more great businesses. So, let's talk. **Visit cms**talklaw**.com**

Let's talk law

C'M'S'

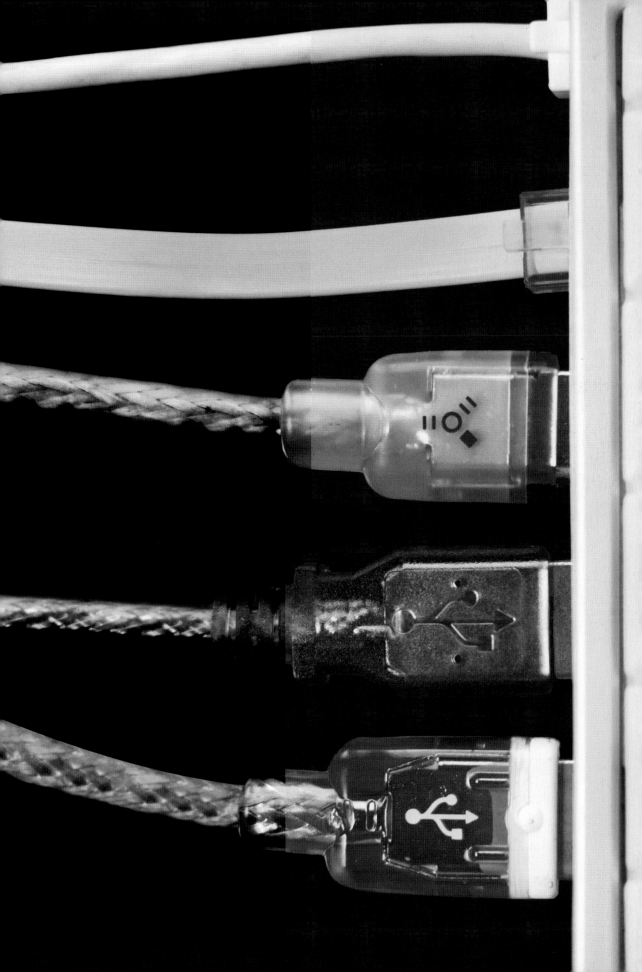

The essential guide to the leading employers recruiting graduates.
NEW EDITION 2002-2003
GRADUATE EMPLOYERS
TOP 100 GRADUATE EMPLOYERS 2005-2006
The definitive guide t recruiting grad
5th EDITION 2003-2004
THE TIMES
TOP 100
GRADUATE EMPLOYERS
THE TIMES
TOP 100
GRADUATE EMPLOYERS
THE TIMES
TOP 100
GRADUATE EMPLOYERS
NEW EDITION FOR 2000-2001
The essential guide to the leading employers recruiting graduates in 1999-2000.
The definitive guide to the leading recruiting graduates during 2006
organisations
00-2001.
GRADUATE EMP
GRADUATE E

Ten Years of Researching Britain's Top Employers

by Martin Birchall
Managing Director, High Fliers Research

A decade ago, Tony Blair was celebrating his first year as Prime Minister, US President Bill Clinton was busy denying having "sexual relations" with Monica Lewinsky, petrol cost an average of 61p per litre, Zoë Ball took charge of the Radio 1 breakfast show, Britain's students finished their degrees with average debts of £2,500 and Cher notched up the year's best-selling single with 'Believe'.

For new graduates fresh out of university, 1998 was a great time to be job hunting. Vacancies shot up by more than 12 per cent, one of the largest year-on-year increases since the late 1980s and starting salaries continued to rise at nearly twice the rate of inflation.

Final year students taking part in *The UK Graduate Careers Survey 1998* – the annual survey of finalists' career aspirations and expectations conducted by High Fliers Research – voted Andersen Consulting the year's top graduate employer and more finalists applied for jobs in management consulting than any other career area.

It is interesting to compare the results of that survey with the similar research carried out with the 'Class of 2008' earlier this year. In 1998 half the top twenty employers that students thought offered the best opportunities for graduates were manufacturing or industrial companies. By contrast, just four of the organisations in this year's top twenty actually make anything – the list is dominated instead by accounting & professional services firms, high street banks and public sector employers.

This year, typical salaries at a *Top 100* graduate employer are £27,000, more than 70 per cent higher than the starting rates for graduates ten years ago. The average then was £15,800 and fewer than 30 employers in the UK offered new recruits packages of £20,000 or more.

Less than a third of finalists used the internet in 1998 to research their career options but half supported local university careers fairs. During the 2007-2008 recruitment season, although over three-quarters of students relied on employers' websites as one of their primary sources of graduate job information, attendances at campus recruitment events remained as strong as ever.

Andersen Consulting is one of just three organisations that have made it to number one in *The Times Top 100 Graduate Employers* in the last ten years. Having stormed to the top spot in 1998 the firm, later known as Accenture, remained there for five consecutive years. Their success heralded a huge surge in popularity for careers in consulting and at its peak in 2001 almost one in six university graduates applied for jobs in the sector.

In the year before the firm changed its name, Andersen Consulting astutely introduced a new graduate package that included a £28,500 starting salary (a sky-high figure for graduates in

IT'S WHERE GRADUATES TURN

**More graduates read The Times
and timesonline.co.uk
than any other national newspaper.***

timesonline.co.uk/jobs

2000) and a much talked-about £10,000 bonus, helping to assure the firm's popularity, irrespective of its corporate branding.

In 2003, after two dismal years in graduate recruitment when vacancies for university-leavers dropped by more than a fifth following the terrorist attacks of 11th September 2001, the Civil Service was named Britain's leading graduate employer. A year later it was displaced by PricewaterhouseCoopers, the accounting and professional services firm formed from the merger of Price Waterhouse and Coopers & Lybrand in 1998. At the time, the firm was the largest private-sector recruiter of graduates, hiring over 1,000 trainees annually.

PricewaterhouseCoopers has now stayed at number one for five years running, increasing its share of the student vote from 5 per cent in 2004 to more than 10 per cent in 2007. This year, however, the firm has faced its stiffest competition yet from rivals Deloitte and retained the top ranking by just seven votes.

PwC's reign as the leading employer represents a remarkable renaissance for the entire accounting sector. Whereas a decade ago, a career in accountancy was widely regarded as a safe, traditional employment choice and the firms themselves were often derided as being 'dull', 'boring' or just 'bean-counters', today's profession is viewed in a very different light. The training required to become a chartered accountant is now seen as a prized business qualification and the sector's leading firms are regularly described as 'prestigious', 'dynamic' and 'international' by undergraduates looking for their first job after university.

Accountancy's transformation is underlined by the fact that fewer than 8 per cent of final year students opted for one of the top six accounting firms in *Top 100* of 1998, compared with the 22 per cent of votes polled by the 'Big Four' firms in this year's list.

A total of 181 different organisations have now appeared within *The Times Top 100 Graduate Employers* since its inception. Just thirty-six of these have made it into the rankings every year since 1998. The most consistent performers over this period have been the Civil Service, KPMG and Accenture each of which have never been lower than 8th place in the league table. Procter & Gamble has also had a formidable record, appearing in every top ten until 2005, and Ernst & Young, IBM and Unilever have each remained within the top quarter of the list throughout.

Arthur Andersen, the now defunct accounting firm, was actually the most consistently ranked employer in the history of the *Top 100*, achieving either 2nd or 3rd place every year between 1998 and the firm's demise in 2002. Pricewaterhouse-Coopers is the only other employer to have appeared within the top three in each of the years in which it has been listed in the *Top 100*.

Not all employers have been so successful. Chemical company ICI, ranked in 20th place in 1998, dropped out of the *Top 100* altogether in 2001 but has made three reappearances since. British Airways fell over eighty places in the years between 1999 and 2004 and high street chemist

Movers & Shakers in the Top 100

Highest New Entries	Highest Climbing Employers
1998 **Microsoft** (38th)	1998 **JPMorgan** (up 8 places)
1999 **Pfizer** (31st)	1999 **Schlumberger** (up 13 places)
2000 **Morgan Stanley** (34th)	2000 **Capital One** (up 32 places)
2001 **Marconi** (36th)	2001 **European Commission** (up 36 places)
2002 **Guinness UDV** (44th)	2002 **WPP** (up 36 places)
2003 **ASDA** (40th)	2003 **Rolls-Royce** (up 37 places)
2004 **Baker & McKenzie** (61st)	2004 **JPMorgan** (up 29 places)
2005 **Penguin** (70th)	2005 **Teach First** (up 22 places)
2006 **Fujitsu** (81st)	2006 **Google** (up 32 places)
2007 **BDO Stoy Hayward** (74th)	2007 **Pfizer** (up 30 places)
2008 **Sky** (76th)	2008 **Co-operative Group** (up 39 places)

Source **The UK Graduate Careers Survey 1998-2008**, High Fliers Research Ltd, based on interviews with 156,521 students.

You don't have to turn lead into gold to impress us. Just toothpaste tubes into tables.

Unilever Graduate Leadership Programme

Visionaries are just as valuable as magicians at Unilever. So if, for example, you could look at the waste from a toothpaste factory in Brazil* and see an opportunity to make chairs, tables, floor tiles and even roofing sheets, you'd fit right in here (*99% of all solid waste generated at the factory is recycled).

That's because creativity is exactly what's made us one of the largest and most successful consumer goods companies in the world. And it's that kind of exciting, out-there, focused kind of thinking that we look for in all of our graduates. Whether you're joining **Supply Chain, Marketing, Customer Development, Innovation & Technology Management, Financial Management or Information Technology** you'll benefit from a whole range of experiences from up to four placements; you'll enjoy world-beating training; and you'll enjoy all the opportunity you need to become a future leader.

So think: could you solve some of the biggest challenges for brands like Lynx, Dove, Walls, Flora, Persil and Ben and Jerry's? Could you hold your own with some of the most talented, creative and inspirational people in the industry? If so, we could transform your career.

Visit **www.unilever.co.uk/careers**

Could it be

Boots has slumped from 6th in 1998 to 75th in this year's rankings. Ford, which was once rated as high as 11th, fell out of the list in 2006 after cancelling its graduate recruitment two years previously.

Twenty-eight employers including well-known names such as Nokia, Philips, the Home Office, Abbey, Coca Cola and British Sugar have the dubious record of having only been ranked in the *Top 100* once during the decade, before disppearing without trace. Marconi had the unusual distinction of being one of the highest-ever new entries in 36th place in 2001, only to vanish from the list entirely the following year.

One of the most spectacular ascendancies within the *Top 100* has been the rise and rise of Aldi which joined the list in 65th place in 2002 and is now ranked 8th in the 2008 league table.

Its eye-catching remuneration package (currently £40,000 plus an Audi A4 car for new graduates joining in 2008) coupled with the lofty job title of 'deputy area manager' for its new recruits and the promise of rapid career progression for those who thrive at the company, have really captured the imagination of increasing numbers of student job hunters.

And Teach First – the innovative scheme which recruits graduates to work in some of the UK's most challenging schools for two years after university before they embark on careers in other areas – has been another runaway success in the rankings. After appearing in the *The Times Top 100 Graduate Employers* as a new entry in 63rd place in 2003, the scheme is currently ranked 9th and is aiming to double the number of graduates it recruits over the next three years.

THE TIMES TOP 100 GRADUATE EMPLOYERS

Winners & Losers in the Top 100

Most Consistent Employers 1998-2008

	Highest Ranking	Lowest Ranking
Arthur Andersen*	2nd (1998-2001)	3rd (2002)
PricewaterhouseCoopers*	1st (2004-2008)	3rd (1999-2001, 2003)
Civil Service	1st (2003)	6th (1998,2008)
KPMG	3rd (2006-2008)	8th (1998, 1999)
Accenture (formerly Andersen Consulting)	1st (1998-2002)	8th (2006)
Ernst & Young	11th (2007, 2008)	21st (1998)
IBM	13th (2000)	25th (1998)
Procter & Gamble	3rd (1998)	15th (2007)
Army	4th (2003)	18th (2007)
GlaxoSmithKline	11th (2000)	26th (1998)

* Employer did not feature in the Top 100 every year between 1998 and 2008

Employers Climbing Highest 1998-2008

	New Entry Ranking	Highest Ranking
Google	85th (2005)	24th (2008)
Aldi	65th (2002)	8th (2008)
Teach First	63rd (2003)	9th (2008)
Oxfam	95th (2003)	45th (2006)
Cancer Research UK	79th (2004)	34th (2008)
Royal Bank of Scotland Group	54th (1999)	15th (2004-2006)
The Co-operative Group	100th (2007)	61st (2008)

Employers Falling Furthest 1998-2008

	Highest Ranking	Lowest Ranking
British Airways	6th (1999)	87th (2004)
Boots	6th (1998)	75th (2007)
Ford	11th (1999)	Not ranked (2006-2008)
ICI	20th (1998)	Not ranked (2001, 2004, 2006-2008)
Ministry of Defence	35th (2003)	Not ranked (2007)
Marconi	36th (2001)	Not ranked (2002-2008)
Logica	39th (1999)	Not ranked (2003-2008)

Source **The UK Graduate Careers Survey 1998-2008**, High Fliers Research Ltd, based on interviews with 156,521 students.

THE TIMES
TOP 100
GRADUATE EMPLOYERS

Top 10 Graduate Employers 1998-2007

1998
1. Andersen Consulting (now Accenture)
2. Arthur Andersen
3. Procter & Gamble
4. Marks & Spencer
5. Civil Service
6. Boots
7. Unilever
8. KPMG
9. Price Waterhouse
10. British Airways

1999
1. Andersen Consulting (now Accenture)
2. Arthur Andersen
3. PricewaterhouseCoopers
4. Procter & Gamble
5. Civil Service
6. British Airways
7. Marks & Spencer
8. KPMG
9. Unilever
10. Boots

2000
1. Andersen Consulting (now Accenture)
2. Arthur Andersen
3. PricewaterhouseCoopers
4. Procter & Gamble
5. KPMG
6. Civil Service
7. Army
8. Unilever
9. Mars
10. BBC

2001
1. Accenture
2. Arthur Andersen
3. PricewaterhouseCoopers
4. Procter & Gamble
5. Goldman Sachs
6. Civil Service
7. KPMG
8. Unilever
9. Army
10. Mars

2002
1. Accenture
2. PricewaterhouseCoopers
3. Andersen (formerly Arthur Andersen)
4. Civil Service
5. Army
6. KPMG
7. Unilever
8. Procter & Gamble
9. Goldman Sachs
10. Mars

2003
1. Civil Service
2. Accenture
3. PricewaterhouseCoopers
4. Army
5. KPMG
6. HSBC
7. BBC
8. Procter & Gamble
9. NHS
10. Deloitte & Touche (now Deloitte)

2004
1. PricewaterhouseCoopers
2. Civil Service
3. Accenture
4. KPMG
5. NHS
6. BBC
7. Army
8. Procter & Gamble
9. HSBC
10. Deloitte

2005
1. PricewaterhouseCoopers
2. Civil Service
3. Accenture
4. KPMG
5. BBC
6. Deloitte
7. NHS
8. HSBC
9. Goldman Sachs
10. Procter & Gamble

2006
1. PricewaterhouseCoopers
2. Deloitte
3. KPMG
4. Civil Service
5. BBC
6. NHS
7. HSBC
8. Accenture
9. Procter & Gamble
10. Goldman Sachs

2007
1. PricewaterhouseCoopers
2. Deloitte
3. KPMG
4. Civil Service
5. BBC
6. NHS
7. Accenture
8. HSBC
9. Aldi
10. Goldman Sachs

Source **The UK Graduate Careers Survey 1998-2007**, High Fliers Research Ltd, based on interviews with 141,140 students.

EXPLORE

KNOWLEDGE TO ACT.
FREEDOM TO ACHIEVE.

Thomson Reuters is the world leader in the knowledge industry.
By combining cutting-edge technology with a focus on innovation, we provide
intelligent information to businesses and professionals worldwide. Delivering
this valued information in a variety of markets means dynamic career opportunities for our employees.

We hire bright people and challenge them to do amazing things. Here, teamwork, friendships and integrity abound. In this fast-paced environment, you'll
work hard, play hard and be encouraged to give back to your community.

At Thomson Reuters, you'll experience a culture of career advancement,
ongoing learning and performance recognition. And though you're working
for one company, you'll discover a world of opportunities.

Visit **careers.thomsonreuters.com** to explore your opportunities.

"Rated the #1 graduate recruitment website"

THE TIMES

TOP 100

GRADUATE EMPLOYERS

Index

	Accountancy	Consulting	Engineering	Finance	General Management	Human Resources	Investment Banking	IT	Law	Logistics	Manufacturing	Marketing	Media	Purchasing	Research & Development	Retailing	Sales	Other
HBOS			●	●	●	●		●				●			●	●		
Herbert Smith									●						●	●		
HSBC				●	●	●		●								●		
IBM	●	●	●					●	●					●				
John Lewis				●	●			●								●		
J.P. Morgan				●	●		●									●		
KPMG	●							●								●		
L'Oréal		●		●								●				●	●	
Linklaters									●									
Lloyds TSB			●	●	●	●		●								●		
Lovells									●									
Marks & Spencer					●			●						●		●		
Mars			●	●	●						●	●		●			●	
McDonald's Restaurants					●											●		
McKinsey & Company		●																
Merrill Lynch			●	●			●	●										
Met Office		●	●	●	●			●			●		●	●				
Metropolitan Police	●		●		●			●			●	●			●			
MI5 – The Security Service			●		●			●										
Microsoft					●			●								●		
Ministry of Defence			●		●			●										
Morgan Stanley				●		●		●										
NGDP for Local Government					●													
NHS					●	●		●										
npower		●	●	●				●										
Oxfam	●				●	●		●				●	●		●			
Penguin	●		●		●				●			●					●	
Police HPDS																		●
PricewaterhouseCoopers	●	●						●	●									
Procter & Gamble			●		●			●		●	●	●		●				
QinetiQ			●					●										
Rolls-Royce			●															
Royal Air Force			●		●	●		●	●	●								
Royal Bank of Scotland Group	●		●	●	●			●				●		●		●		
Royal Navy			●	●	●	●		●	●	●				●		●		
Sainsbury's				●				●			●			●		●		
Shell			●	●				●										
Sky			●	●				●				●						
Slaughter and May									●									
Teach First	●	●	●	●	●	●	●	●	●		●	●				●		
Tesco	●	●	●	●	●			●		●	●	●		●		●	●	
Thomson Reuters	●			●				●				●					●	
Transport for London	●	●	●	●	●			●			●	●		●				
UBS					●	●		●										
Unilever			●	●				●			●						●	
Watson Wyatt		●		●	●													
WPP Group												●	●					

accenture

High performance. Delivered.

accenture.com/ukgraduates

Vacancies for around 500 graduates in 2009

- Consulting
- IT

Starting salary for 2009
£31,000
Plus £10,000 bonus.

Universities Accenture plans to visit in 2008-9
Aston, Bath, Birmingham, Bristol, Cambridge, Durham, Edinburgh, Exeter, Glasgow, Leeds, London, Loughborough, Manchester, Newcastle, Nottingham, Oxford, St Andrews, Warwick
Please check with your university careers service for details of events.

Application deadline
Year-round recruitment

Contact Details
✉ ukgraduates@accenture.com
☎ 0500 100 189
Turn to page 256 now to request more information or visit our new website at www.top100graduateemployers.com

With over 178,000 people working in 49 countries, Accenture is one of the world's leading management consulting, technology services and outsourcing organisations.

They combine unparalleled experience and comprehensive capabilities with extensive research to work with clients helping them become high-performance businesses. Their work invariably involves the application of information technology to business challenges.

Accenture believe that they offer great opportunities for graduates, partly because of the work they do, and partly because learning and personal development are so high on their agenda. Graduate joiners will be able to build core business, technology and industry expertise whilst controlling their own development. Promotion is based entirely on the skills acquired and the contribution made, and flexible working programmes allow them to manage their schedule to suit them.

They also actively encourage people to get involved in community and charitable activities that make a real difference to communities across the UK and around the world.

Accenture look for people with more than just excellent academics. They need individuals who are passionate about something outside their studies, who have some work experience and a strong interest in business and technology.
For graduates who meet the above criteria, expect to achieve a 2:1 degree and have 320 UCAS points or equivalent, they can offer a truly rounded career.

They also have a number of schemes and placements that are designed to give an insider's view of the world of Accenture. Find out more at accenture.com/ukschemes

Often, a fresh angle is the solution.
Just another day at the office for a Tiger.

Join Accenture for a career that keeps you motivated and moving forward. Work on vital assignments for top class clients and help them to achieve high performance. Push yourself, while developing your skills and confidence. Work with the best people worldwide to solve problems and do what hasn't been done before. If this is your idea of a typical working day, Accenture is the place to work.

Graduate Careers in Consulting

Almost everything we do involves the application of IT to business challenges. But that's not to say you have to be a computer genius to get on here (although we certainly wouldn't hold it against you). If you're genuinely interested in business and technology, expect to achieve a 2:1 degree, in any degree discipline, and have 320 UCAS points or equivalent, we can offer you a truly rounded career.

As well as doing interesting, challenging work with exceptional people, using the latest technology, we offer unrivalled training and you will be able to develop faster here than almost anywhere else. What's more you'll be rewarded well with a salary of £31,000 and an additional £10,000 bonus.

We also encourage you to get involved in charitable activities

that make a real difference to communities throughout the world.

For people with the right intelligence and personal qualities, consulting is possibly the best job in the world. Discover more and apply online by visiting our website.

Accenture is committed to being an equal opportunities employer.

Visit accenture.com/ukgraduates

• Consulting • Technology • Outsourcing

accenture

High performance. Delivered.

ADDLESHAW GODDARD

www.addleshawgoddard.com/graduates

**Vacancies for around
50 graduates in 2009**
For training contracts starting in 2011

 Law

Starting salary for 2009
£24,750-£36,000

**Universities that
Addleshaw Goddard
plans to visit in 2008-9**
Birmingham, Bristol,
Cambridge, Cardiff,
Durham, Edinburgh,
Leeds, Leicester, Liverpool,
London, Manchester,
Newcastle, Nottingham,
Oxford, Reading, Sheffield,
St Andrews, Warwick, York
Please check with your university
careers service for details of events.

Application deadline
31st July 2009

Contact Details
✉ grad@addleshawgoddard.com

Turn to page 256 now to request more
information or visit our new website at
www.top100graduateemployers.com

A leading national law firm with the capability to provide
excellent service to a global client base. Ranked 15th largest
law firm in the UK, Addleshaw Goddard is also ranked in The
Sunday Times Best Companies To Work For.

The firm has four main practice areas: corporate, finance and projects,
real estate and contentious and commercial.

Addleshaw Goddard are looking for graduates and undergraduates from any
academic discipline who possess the motivation and commitment necessary
to join a top 20 law firm and who are capable of achieving, or have achieved,
at least a 2(i) degree.

During their training contract, trainees will be given the opportunity to
experience a broad range of corporate and commercial work. During each
six-month seat they will have regular performance reviews with their supervisor,
and the on-the-job training will be supported by courses provided by the firm's
in-house team and external experts.

Tuition fees are paid for both GDL and LPC courses, together with an annual
maintenance grant – currently £7,000 per course for all future trainees studying
GDL or LPC in central London, and £4,500 per course for all future trainees
studying elsewhere.

They have vacation schemes in their London, Leeds and Manchester
offices both at Easter and Summer. For an invaluable insight into the firm
and help deciding whether Addleshaw Goddard is the right destination,
visit www.addleshawgoddard.com/graduates

ADDLESHAW GODDARD

EAGER

Help us grow as a team. We'll help you grow as an individual.

As a fast expanding and innovative law firm, a career with Addleshaw Goddard means more variety, earlier responsibility and greater future opportunities to develop with the firm. Training with us will mean working with top FTSE companies and other leading organisations.

But it's not just about hard work. We care about maintaining a balanced culture. The proof; our support for employees has resulted in The Sunday Times listing Addleshaw Goddard as one of its 'Top 100 Best Companies To Work For' in 2008.

With offices in London, Leeds and Manchester, we can offer quality training wherever you want to be based. If you are interested in a training contract with us or a Summer/Easter placement visit:

www.addleshawgoddard.com/graduates

AIRBUS

Vacancies for around 50-80 graduates in 2009

- Engineering
- Finance
- Human Resources
- Logistics
- Manufacturing
- Purchasing

Starting salary for 2009
£23,500+
Welcome bonus of £2,750.

Universities that Airbus plans to visit in 2008-9
Bath, Belfast, Birmingham, Bristol, City, Leeds, Liverpool, London, Loughborough, Manchester, Nottingham, Sheffield, Southampton, Warwick
Please check with your university careers service for details of events.

Application deadline
See website for full details.

Contact Details
✉ airbusuk-grad@airbus.com

Turn to page 256 now to request more information or visit our new website at www.top100graduateemployers.com

Airbus is one of the world's leading companies for the design and manufacture of aircraft. With the new double-deck A380 recently entering service, and design and development work well advanced on the new A350 XWB (extra-wide body), which is due to enter service in 2013, cutting edge innovation and technology is vital for uncompromising, environmentally-responsible, 21st century aircraft designs.

Forecasts of strong, continued growth in air travel and high demand for civil aircraft in the decades ahead, mean Airbus offers exciting challenges for talented men and women in engineering and customer facing roles to join a vibrant business; helping to continue to push the boundaries and to create an exciting, sustainable, eco-efficient future for civil aviation.

Open-minded and customer-focused graduates will enjoy the chance to develop their talents and experience on the Airbus UK Direct Entry Graduate Scheme (DEG). The scheme develops detailed knowledge of a business function through structured placements in the UK and Europe, with strategic partners, customers and suppliers. Though the programme format is consistent, individual programmes can depend on the function joined, experience, interests and current business challenges.

Through the scheme and beyond graduates will have access to excellent, focused training and support to help achieve membership of professional institutions, further qualifications and long-term career planning. Involvement in education and community projects to broaden experience and skills is encouraged.

Our innovation,
Your potential.

Over the next 20 years, the world's airlines will need more than 24,000 new aircraft, which must be greener, cleaner, quieter and smarter than ever before.

With a record of technological advances that includes fly-by-wire and the first time in the history of aviation that a commercial aircraft flew on an alternative 'gas to liquid' fuel, Airbus is continuing to set the pace. Attracting, developing and sharing the highest standards of talent is vital in ensuring that the world's aircraft are as efficient and as environmentally responsible as possible throughout their entire lifecycle.

Every year we look for new and recent, high-achieving graduates to join our Direct Entry Graduate Scheme (DEG). This scheme is a 2 year training programme (except Finance, which is a 3 year programme) designed to develop graduates, both personally and professionally. You would receive support and guidance in areas such as business and cultural awareness, personal effectiveness and technical understanding. You would also receive support to gain professional accreditation.

Our Internship Programme encourages undergraduates to join us for a duration of 3, 6 or 12 months and is designed to give you the opportunity, as part of your studies, to put into practice the theoretical knowledge you are acquiring. It is also an excellent opportunity to bring new ideas and experiences into the organisation.

For more information about the opportunities available and key application deadlines, please visit our website.

We are an Equal Opportunities Employer.

www.airbus-careers.com

Airbus. Setting the standards.

Vacancies for around
90-100 graduates in 2009

General Management

Retailing

Starting salary for 2009
£40,000

Universities that Aldi
plans to visit in 2008-9
Birmingham, Bristol,
Cardiff, Dublin, Durham,
Glasgow, Leeds, Liverpool,
London, Manchester,
Sheffield, Southampton
Please check with your university
careers service for details of events.

Application deadline
Year-round recruitment

Contact Details
✉ recruitment.nes@aldi.co.uk

Turn to page 256 now to request more
information or visit our new website at
www.top100graduateemployers.com

Aldi, one of the world's top retailers with 7,000 stores worldwide is continually searching for outstanding graduates who enjoy making decisions and take real satisfaction from achieving results.

Aldi offers an unrivalled Graduate Training Programme which really stands out from other UK retailers. The market leading package provides graduates with comprehensive training for the role of Area Manager. Graduates begin with an individual twelve month training plan which quickly introduces them to the dynamic and demanding world of retail business management from store operations through to administration, logistics and property.

During the training graduates develop leadership qualities, commercial awareness, technical and management skills with a strong focus on and understanding of customer satisfaction and business efficiency.

Graduate trainees have the opportunity to manage a store within weeks, progressing quickly to managing a multi-million pound area of four to six stores as if it were their own business.

With the opportunity of a two year secondment in Europe or further afield plus a chance of directorship after five years, Aldi stands out from other retailers in giving its graduates high levels of responsibility from day one.

Recruiting confident, ambitious and enthusiastic individuals, Aldi offers successful graduates a challenging yet rewarding training programme, complete with variety, ownership and job satisfaction. Motivated to excel in all disciplines, it may be demanding at the top but worth it when successful applicants experience the rewards.

You can't get sweeter than our sweetener

To make a 500g jar of honey, a bee would have to fly the equivalent of three times around the world. To collect our sweetener of £40,000, you'll have to put in the miles too. But, Aldi will give you an Audi A4 to help. In fact, we'll give you all the encouragement and support we can. Because we will both have invested a lot of time and energy in making your career a success. But what we can't do is create the drive, determination, desire and pure undiluted talent needed to make a success of the Aldi Graduate Area Manager Training Programme. That will be down to you – and you alone. So yes, the package is eye-catching and attractive. But you'll earn it. And if you do have to work hard, what better place than a global business that's in the Top 10 of 'The Times Top 100 Graduate Employers'?

aldi.co.uk/recruitment

Graduate
Area Manager
£40,000
rising to
£57,750
after three years
Fully expensed
Audi A4
Opportunity
for directorship
within 5 years
International
secondment
opportunities

ALLEN & OVERY

Vacancies for around 120 graduates in 2009

For training contracts starting in 2011

■ Law

Starting salary for 2009
£37,000

Universities Allen & Overy plans to visit in 2008-9

Bath, Birmingham, Bristol, Brunel, Cambridge, Cardiff, City, Dublin, Durham, East Anglia, Edinburgh, Exeter, Kent, Leeds, Leicester, Liverpool, London, Manchester, Newcastle, Northumbria, Nottingham, Oxford, Reading, Sheffield, Southampton, St Andrews, Warwick, York

Please check with your university careers service for details of events.

Application deadline
Year-round recruitment

Contact Details

✉ graduate.recruitment
@allenovery.com

☎ 020 3088 0000

Turn to page 256 now to request more information or visit our new website at
www.top100graduateemployers.com

Allen & Overy is an international legal practice with over 5,000 people in 29 major centres worldwide. The practice's client list includes many of the world's top businesses, financial institutions, governments and private individuals.

Allen & Overy is world renowned for the high quality of its banking, corporate and international capital markets advice, but also has major strengths in dispute resolution, tax, employment and benefits, real estate and private client. Within its broad range of expertise, the practice offers a training contract characterised by flexibility and choice. Training contracts are tailored for each trainee to ensure they have the best start to their career.

Given the strength of the practice's international finance practice, trainees spend at least 12 months working in banking, corporate and international capital markets, with contentious experience in either dispute resolution or employment. There are also opportunities for trainees to undertake an international or client secondment in their second year of training. By working closely with trainers and other colleagues, trainees develop practical experience and enjoy a high level of early responsibility.

Vital to Allen & Overy's success is the way they approach work. Allen & Overy people enjoy what they do and want to employ people who have initiative while maintaining a professional, supportive and friendly working environment.

Allen & Overy recruits approximately 120 trainee solicitors and approximately 120 vacation students (winter, spring and summer) each year. Applications are welcome from both law and non-law candidates. At least a 2.1 degree (or equivalent) should be predicted or acheived, with evidence of teamwork, leadership, motivation and problem-solving demonstrated.

▲ Arcadia Group Limited

Vacancies for around 250 graduates in 2009

- Finance
- General Management
- Human Resources
- Logistics
- Purchasing
- Retailing

Starting salary for 2009
£17,500-£23,000

Universities Arcadia Group plans to visit in 2008-9
Please check with your university careers service for details of events.

Application deadline
See website for full details.

Contact Details
✉ management.programmes @arcadiagroup.co.uk
Turn to page 256 now to request more information or visit our new website at www.top100graduateemployers.com

The Arcadia Group is the UK's largest privately owned fashion retailer with over 2,500 outlets and 27,000 employees. Owning eight of the high street's best-known fashion brands – Burton, Dorothy Perkins, Evans, Miss Selfridge, Outfit, Topman, Topshop and Wallis, there's something for everyone.

Arcadia offers a variety of opportunities for graduates with a range of skills, from the numerically minded to those that are entrepreneurial or creative with an eye for trends. Opportunities are available across retail management, buying, merchandising, distribution, finance and human resources.

Arcadia recognise that developing the right knowledge, skills and behaviours in people is vital to its success. Graduates receive on the job competency based training, specially designed development programmes, and where appropriate support for formal qualifications, e.g. CIMA/ACCA and CIPD. With this combination of on-and-off-the-job training, graduates are able to take control of their development and progress quickly.

Arcadia is looking for the brightest and most talented graduates to join its team. As well as formal qualifications, successful candidates will demonstrate commercial awareness, be a great team player, have excellent communication skills and most importantly have ambition and desire for responsibility. A passion for customer service and fashion retail is also vital and is best demonstrated through appropriate work experience.

As Arcadia recognise the importance of rewarding individuals for their contribution, successful candidates will receive a competitive salary, up to 25 days holiday, 25% discount on group merchandise, participation in the bonus scheme and membership of the group's pension scheme.

CAREERS THAT SET THE TREND

Are you enterprising and bursting with energy?
Do you enjoy life lived on fast-forward?
Are you creative, passionate and determined to succeed?

If the answer is "yes", then a career in retail is for you.

The Arcadia Group is the UK's largest privately owned fashion retailer with more than 2,500 outlets. We own eight of the high street's best-known fashion brands and offer a host of exciting career opportunities in Retail Management, Buying, Merchandising, Distribution, Finance and Human Resources.

Why join us? Not only will you enjoy an exciting benefits package, through ongoing development you'll have the opportunity to progress within a business that is at the forefront of fashion retail.

Interested? Then don't miss out. Apply online at:
www.arcadiagroup.co.uk/careers

BURTON   DOROTHY PERKINS   evans.   Miss Selfridge   OUTFIT   TOPSHOP   **TOPMAN**   wallis

ARMY
BE THE BEST
REGULAR & TERRITORIAL

Vacancies for around 700 graduates in 2009

- Engineering
- Finance
- General Management
- Human Resources
- IT
- Logistics

Starting salary for 2009
£28,960
On completion of officer training at Sandhurst.

Universities the Army plans to visit in 2008-9
Please check with your university careers service for details of events.

Application deadline
Year-round recruitment

Contact Details
☎ 0845 7300 111
Turn to page 256 now to request more information or visit our new website at www.top100graduateemployers.com

Being an Army Officer is unlike any other job – from leading a platoon of 30 soldiers one week to organising a team on adventurous training the next. The Army engages with graduates and trains them to become some of the best leaders in the world.

As one of the most respected and technologically advanced organisations in the world, the Army can offer unrivalled training and development to graduates of all disciplines, enhancing management and leadership potential and providing the skills and self-confidence to excel in the Army and, later on, in civilian careers.

Beyond the many career-enhancing qualities in which graduates become skilled, there are many personal rewards for most Officers – they will find it incredibly satisfying to discover what they're capable of under different kinds of pressure. After just one year of training, Officers can be responsible for over 30 soldiers and several million pounds' worth of equipment.

Graduates start their Officer training at the Royal Military Academy Sandhurst where they learn all aspects of soldiering, management and leadership training. On completion, they will join their Regiment or Corps where they will undergo specialist training for their chosen occupation. Subsequently, Officers may study for Army-sponsored or vocational qualifications.

If the career development isn't enough to tempt them, perhaps some of the other aspects of being an Officer will – the Army provides a challenging career, continuous professional development, great promotional prospects, unrivalled travel, sporting and adventure opportunities. There is also great camaraderie and lasting friendships to be made.

GTE PIAD FRO SLVONIG PMLEBROS.

If you enjoy a challenge and are looking for an exciting and rewarding lifestyle, the Army might be for you. Each year, the Army recruits over 700 potential officers into Sandhurst. Some will make the Army their career, others will stay a few years; both will benefit from excellent leadership and management training, fast promotion opportunities, six weeks paid annual leave and lasting friendships. Most will enter Sandhurst as graduates, many having received financial sponsorship from the Army through university, while others take advantage of opportunities to study post graduate qualifications on full pay.

ARMY OFFICER. HAVE YOU GOT WHAT IT TAKES?

ARMY
BE THE BEST
REGULAR & TERRITORIAL

ARUP

www.arup.com

Vacancies for around
220 graduates in 2009

- Consulting
- Engineering

Vacancies also available in Europe, Asia and the USA.

Starting salary for 2009
£24,000

Universities that Arup plans to visit in 2008-9
Bath, Belfast, Birmingham, Bristol, Cambridge, Cardiff, Durham, Edinburgh, Heriot-Watt, Leeds, Liverpool, Manchester, Newcastle, Nottingham, Sheffield, Strathclyde, Warwick
Please check with your university careers service for details of events.

Application deadline
Year-round recruitment

Contact Details
✉ gradrec@arup.com

Turn to page 256 now to request more information or visit our new website at www.top100graduateemployers.com

Arup is a global firm of designers, engineers, planners and business consultants providing a diverse range of professional services to clients around the world. Arup's innovative and fully-integrated approach brings their full complement of skills and knowledge to bear on any given design problem.

They exert a significant influence on the built environment and are the creative force behind many of the world's most innovative and sustainable designs. Examples of Arup projects are: the Beijing National Stadium and National Aquatics Centre, Sydney Opera House, the Millennium Bridge, the Swiss Re Headquarters and the City of Manchester Stadium.

Arup has almost 9,000 staff working in 92 offices in more than 37 countries. At any one time, they have over 10,000 projects running concurrently.

A commitment to the environment and the communities being worked in has always been at the heart of the Arup ethos. It defines their approach to their work, to their clients and collaborators, and to each other.

Their ethos is summarised in the aims of the firm, set out by Ove Arup in his key speech of 1970. Arup will ensure that the Arup name is always associated with quality; they will act honestly and fairly in dealing with their staff and others; and they will enhance prosperity for all Arup staff.

Arup recruits over 200 graduates in the UK every year and has graduate vacancies in architecture, engineering and planning roles, there are also vacancies throughout the rest of the world.

For further information please visit www.arup.com

at arup

we lead never follow

work with the brightest minds

develop innovative solutions like using displacement ventilation to minimise energy use at the Antwerp Law Courts

pursue opportunities in more than 20 disciplines

have the freedom to be creative and to learn

don't do things like everyone else

follow your own path

Committed to equal opportunities
www.arup.com

ARUP

ASDA

www.asdagraduates.com

Vacancies for around 50 graduates in 2009

- Finance
- General Management
- IT
- Logistics
- Marketing
- Purchasing
- Retailing

Starting salary for 2009
£23,000

Universities that ASDA plans to visit in 2008-9
Leeds, Manchester, Sheffield
Please check with your university careers service for details of events.

Application deadline
1st March 2009

Contact Details
Turn to page 256 now to request more information or visit our new website at www.top100graduateemployers.com

There's more to ASDA than meets the eye. Part of Wal-Mart, the biggest retailer in the world, ASDA has over 160,000 colleagues, nearly 400 stores and a whole host of graduate opportunities.

At ASDA everyone has a vital role to play in meeting the needs of over 16 million customers every week, whether they work in Logistics, Finance, Marketing or in store. After all retail isn't all about boxes and barcodes. There are all sorts of interesting projects to get involved in, such as eco-stores, local sourcing and home shopping.

Every day is different and offers new challenges as ASDA graduates take on key roles and make a real contribution from day one. The culture is friendly, lively and open. Ideas are listened to and successes are celebrated in an ever-changing environment where anything is possible. One of the UK's fastest growing retailers, ASDA values people with a passion for service and the determination to work hard, have fun and progress quickly. Put simply they value people who can ensure that there's no place like ASDA.

ASDA's graduate scheme offers exciting opportunities in a variety of areas from Retail Management and Retail Development to Trading, Finance and Marketing. Not to mention ecommerce, Logistics Management and Project Management Systems Solutions.

All types of degrees are welcomed and all kinds of ambitions can be achieved. So discover more about the unique culture, fantastic opportunities and amazing careers at ASDA.

THINK BEYOND

Is retail all black and white? Is it all barcodes and boxes, scanning and sorting? Or is there something more? Something complex, colourful, intriguing, vibrant? Something sustainable, inspiring and full of endless possibilities? Something that could take you further than most other graduate careers could? Think beyond the barcode. Think ASDA and visit www.asdagraduates.com

there's no place like **ASDA**

www.ideas.astrazeneca.com

I want
to be
recognised

**Vacancies for around
15-25 graduates in 2009**

Engineering

Finance

IT

Logistics

Marketing

Purchasing

Research & Development

Starting salary for 2009
£25,000-£28,000

**Universities AstraZeneca
plans to visit in 2008-9**
Please check with your university
careers service for details of events.

Application deadline
Year-round recruitment
See website for full details.

Contact Details
Turn to page 256 now to request more
information or visit our new website at
www.top100graduateemployers.com

One of the world's leading pharmaceutical companies,
AstraZeneca turns great ideas into innovative medicines which
make real difference to peoples lives.

The company's excellent reputation and diversity of graduate opportunities
make them the natural choice for candidates from a science background.
However, their strengths in manufacturing and commerce mean they can also
provide challenges to graduates from other disciplines. Whatever their degree
subject, graduates will be excited by the quality and diversity of opportunity.
Programmes are designed to progress careers through an integrated range of
flexible training activities and blended learning ideas.

From day-one induction and personal mentoring to management and global
leadership programmes, AstraZeneca provides the resources and support
graduates need to reach their full potential; while cross-functional moves,
secondments and international assignments can broaden the experience.
It's a performance-based culture with competitive salaries and bonuses that
are linked to overall progress. But they also believe that quality of life and
quality of work go hand in hand. That's why they actively pursue opportunities
for flexible working arrangements.

Core benefits include a minimum level of pension contribution and healthcare
provision, and the additional range of 'rewards options' is considerable. But
these are benefits that people tend to appreciate further down the line. What
probably excites graduates more at this stage is the opportunity to develop
their skills within a truly global business that's setting the standards in an
industry rich in challenges and rewards.

I want
to go
further

Graduate opportunities, all disciplines.

It's only possible to achieve your full potential when you're given the proper support and resources. At AstraZeneca, we're committed to our graduates' success and reward people on the basis of performance.

take your ambitions forward at
ideas.astrazeneca.com
sign up for job alerts and let the opportunities come to you

AstraZeneca
life inspiring ideas

ATKINS

Vacancies for around 300 graduates in 2009

Engineering

Starting salary for 2009
£Varies by function
See website for full details.

Universities that Atkins plans to visit in 2008-9

Bath, Belfast, Birmingham, Bristol, Cambridge, Cardiff, Dundee, Durham, Glasgow, Heriot-Watt, Leeds, Leicester, Liverpool, London, Loughborough, Manchester, Newcastle, Northumbria, Nottingham, Nottingham Trent, Oxford, Oxford Brookes, Reading, Sheffield, Southampton, Strathclyde, Surrey, Swansea, Ulster, Warwick
Please check with your university careers service for details of events.

Application deadline
Year-round recruitment

Contact Details

✉ graduates@atkinsglobal.com

☎ 0121 483 6233

Turn to page 256 now to request more information or visit our new website at www.top100graduateemployers.com

Atkins is a multinational design and engineering consultancy, providing expertise to help resolve complex challenges presented by the built and natural environment. Whether it's the concept for a new skyscraper, the upgrade of a rail network, the modelling of a flood defence system or the improvement of a management process, they plan, design and enable solutions.

Atkins is increasingly focussed on Carbon Critical Design. The Dubai International Financial Centre (DIFC) Lighthouse, for example, will be Dubai's first low-carbon commercial tower. Their expertise also has a direct impact on people's everyday lives, like the detailed design Atkins provided to St. Germans Pumping Station, a key part of the UK's flood protection.

Atkins' graduate programme lets graduates choose how their career unfolds. Gaining invaluable, 'real-world' experience, they'll achieve professional accreditation alongside some of the industry's brightest people. A mentor will help them shape their development and they'll be part of a lively graduate community.

Atkins is a great place for graduates who aim higher. They're in The Sunday Times 20 Best Big Companies to Work For in the UK, and for the third year running they were voted Most Popular Graduate Recruiter in Construction at the TARGET National Graduate Recruitment Awards. And Atkins feature again in the Top 50 Places Where Women Want to Work.

For more information about the exciting careers at Atkins and how to apply, visit www.atkinsglobal.com/graduates

ATKINS

Aerospace
Architecture
Building Design
Building Surveying
Communication & Systems
Conventional Power
Cost & Project Management
Defence
Development Infrastructure
Environment
Geotechnics & Tunnelling
Highways
Intelligent Transport Systems
Management Consultancy
Nuclear Power
Oil & Gas
Rail & Metro
Transport Planning
Water

AIM HIGHER

Join our Graduate Development Programme and together we'll build a brighter future for everyone. Instead of leading you down a set career path, we'll open doors by giving you choices about how your career unfolds and providing an unmatched breadth of projects to gain experience on.

If you share our boundless curiosity and drive to improve the world in which we all live, work and play, it's a chance to become an expert in whatever inspires you most.

Make the story of your career a more interesting one. To find out more and apply, visit **www.atkinsglobal.com/graduates**

Plan Design Enable

BAE SYSTEMS

www.baesystems.com/graduates

Vacancies for around
300 graduates in 2009

- Engineering
- Finance
- Human Resources
- IT
- Logistics
- Manufacturing
- Marketing
- Purchasing
- Research & Development
- Sales

Starting salary for 2009
£23,000-£27,500

Universities BAE Systems
plans to visit in 2008-9
Bath, Bristol, Brunel, Cambridge, Cardiff, City, Durham, Edinburgh, Glasgow, Lancaster, Leeds, Leicester, Liverpool, Loughborough, Manchester, Newcastle, Nottingham, Nottingham Trent, Sheffield, Southampton, Strathclyde, Warwick
Please check with your university careers service for details of events.

Application deadline
Year-round recruitment

Contact Details
Turn to page 256 now to request more information or visit our new website at www.top100graduateemployers.com

BAE Systems is the premier global defence and aerospace company delivering a full range of products and services for air, land and naval forces, as well as advanced electronics, information technology solutions and customer support services. With 96,000 employees, and customers in over 100 countries, BAE Systems' sales exceeded £15 billion in 2006.

In the exciting arena of international defence, BAE Systems offers a wealth of opportunities for both graduates and undergraduates.

BAE Systems has three graduate entry programmes; GDF is the main programme, FLDP for those looking for a finance leadership career and Sigma for fast track international leadership.

Most graduates will join the Graduate Development Framework (GDF), which is a two-year scheme. Successful applicants will receive on-the-job training from some of the most talented people in the industry. They will work on real projects offering real responsibility.

For graduates who need to spend a year in industry as part of their degree, BAE Systems offers Industrial Placements in engineering, technology, business and finance. As well as giving a fascinating insight into the workings of the global business, the exposure, responsibility and experiences they provide will give students a real advantage over their fellow peers.

To find out more about BAE Systems' projects, opportunities and entry requirements, please visit www.baesystems.com/graduates where application forms can be submitted.

IMAGINE DEVELOPING A SUBMARINE THAT WEIGHS 8,000 TONNES, CAN DIVE DOWN TO MORE THAN 200 METRES, AND WON'T EVER NEED RE-FUELLING.

www.baesystems.com/graduates

THE NEXT GENERATION IS YOURS.

Graduate opportunities across the UK

Now you see it, now you don't. Our Astute class submarines can stay submerged for 90 days at a time, remaining undetected thousands of miles from home and hundreds of metres underwater. If you have the vision to make the seemingly impossible possible, you could soon be creating or supporting the next generation of defence systems – on land, in the air and at sea.

Visit www.baesystems.com/graduates to see what your imagination could achieve.

BAE SYSTEMS

REAL INNOVATION. REAL ADVANTAGE.

Bank of America

Vacancies for around
100 graduates in 2009

- Finance
- Human Resources
- Investment Banking
- IT
- Marketing
- Sales

Starting salary for 2009
£Competitive

Universities that
Bank of America
plans to visit in 2008-9
Cambridge, City, Durham,
London, Manchester, Oxford,
Strathclyde, Warwick
Please check with your university
careers service for details of events.

Application deadline
14th November 2008

Contact Details
✉ graduates@bankofamerica.com

Turn to page 256 now to request more
information or visit our new website at
www.top100graduateemployers.com

Choose.
Connect.
Grow.

Bank of America
Bank of Opportunity™

Bank of America is one of the world's largest financial institutions, serving all levels of clients from individual consumers to large corporations with a full range of banking, investing, asset management and other financial products and services.

The bank is currently seeking graduate applications for positions across diverse lines of business, including Investment Banking, Global Markets, Technology, Europe Card Services and Risk. Successful applicants will receive induction training in London, Chester, Charlotte or New York. This tuition will combine classroom training with group and individual projects led by industry experts, where graduates will learn technical and professional skills and also more about Bank of America's capabilities and culture.

New graduate starters will have access to ongoing education, either online or in the classroom, which will help them to build long term success. Bank of America's full-time programmes are designed to equip graduates with the personal and business skills required to be successful in the financial services industry. But there is no substitute for what new hires learn whilst working everyday through delivering on targets and interacting with associates across the bank.

It is the quality of Bank of America's people that enables the company to develop strong, lasting relationships with clients, to understand their needs and to create innovative solutions to achieve their goals. The bank seeks candidates who demonstrate a combination of academic aptitude, quantitative skills, strategic and creative thinking with a team focus and the dedication to building a career in the financial services industry.

www.inspiredbybarclays.com

Vacancies for around
230 graduates in 2009

Accountancy

Finance

General Management

Human Resources

IT

Marketing

Retailing

Sales

Starting salary for 2009
£24,000
Plus £3,500 joining bonus and
£3,550 mobility allowance.

Universities that Barclays
plans to visit in 2008-9
Aston, Bath, Bristol,
Cambridge, Durham,
Edinburgh, Leeds, London,
Loughborough, Manchester,
Nottingham, Oxford,
Sheffield, Warwick
Please check with your university
careers service for details of events.

Application deadline
31st December 2008

Contact Details
✉ barclays.graduates@reed.co.uk
Turn to page 256 now to request more
information or visit our new website at
www.top100graduateemployers.com

Barclays spirit of innovation inspires groundbreaking ideas that move the entire industry forward. Whether it's reaching untapped markets, capitalising on the latest technology, launching futuristic new retail bank branches or introducing imaginative products like the carbon-neutral debit card, Barclays always seem to get there first. Not surprisingly their fresh-thinking approach also makes them an inspirational place to develop a graduate career.

That could be Commercial Bank, Retail Banking, Barclaycard, Finance, Treasury, Technology, Tax, HR, UK Retail Marketing. Each business area runs its own structured training programme lasting between one and two years. Graduates will get a real insight into how the area operates, enjoy a high profile and learn from business leaders.

Barclays look for a strong academic background. But the right attitude is just as important as a quick brain. Graduates must be ambitious and focused with the drive and initiative to improve on what's gone before. What has been done outside of academia – placements, gap years, voluntary work or sporting or cultural activities for example – will also help Barclays decide whether applicants have the potential to make a real impact on their business.

Expect formal training, on-the-job learning, study leave to help gain professional qualifications and up to £2,000 to invest in personal development that's relevant to the role. What's more, graduate development won't stop when the programme ends. Career-long learning is a way of life at Barclays and will encourage successful applicants to really make a mark and get on.

WE DON'T LET GOOD IDEAS GET AWAY

We're quick. And we can always spot them. That's why we're behind so many industry firsts. And why we're always getting better at everything we do – from product development to social responsibility projects to helping you get ahead. It's also the reason we're a global bank with plenty of room for people who not only know good ideas when they see them, but who can come up with them in the first place. Wherever you join us, we'll push you to push us.

Graduate careers in Commercial Bank, Retail Banking, Barclaycard, Finance, Treasury, Technology, Tax, HR, UK Retail Marketing.

Pretty inspiring stuff. www.inspiredbybarclays.com

BARCLAYS CAPITAL

**Vacancies for around
500 graduates in 2009**

- Finance
- Human Resources
- Investment Banking
- IT
- Law
- Marketing

Vacancies also available in Europe,
Asia and the USA.

Starting salary for 2009
£Competitive

**Universities that
Barclays Capital
plans to visit in 2008-9**
Bath, Bristol,
Cambridge, Durham,
Edinburgh, London,
Manchester, Nottingham,
Oxford, Reading,
St Andrews, Warwick
Please check with your university
careers service for details of events.

Application deadline
Year-round recruitment

Contact Details
Turn to page 256 now to request more
information or visit our new website at
www.top100graduateemployers.com

EXPECT EXCELLENCE

Barclays Capital is the investment banking division of Barclays Bank PLC, and provides large corporate, government and institutional clients with solutions to their financing and risk management needs.

Barclays Capital has offices in 29 countries, employs over 16,200 people and has the global reach and distribution power to meet the needs of issuers and investors worldwide. Graduate and internship positions are offered in areas across the bank from Compliance to Corporate Real Estate to Investment Banking and Trading.

The graduate programme is key to the success of Barclays Capital and is supported by senior management throughout the organisation. On the programme, graduates are provided with an excellent understanding of financial markets, as well as the bank's products, instruments and services. The programme takes learning one step further, incorporating practical applications through a variety of case studies, workshops and presentations.

As well as full-time opportunities, internships are offered and take place for 10 weeks over the summer. Off-cycle positions are also available, according to business needs. Interns are expected to work on a range of projects, from live transactions and marketing projects, to research and analysis, depending on the business area. As well as the everyday work, interns receive training before and during the programme, and have many opportunities to network with colleagues, recent graduates and senior members of the firm.

M**IOCRITY

EXPECT EXCELLENCE

In our book, it's a dirty word. Average? Middling?
Don't be so rude. At Barclays Capital, we believe the
only acceptable way to do business is to strive for
perfection in everything you do. The result? In just
11 years, we've grown from a new operation into one
of the world's leading investment banks. And there's
nothing mediocre about that. Find out how much
you could achieve at barcap.com/expectexcellence

barcap.com/expectexcellence   EARN SUCCESS EVERY DAY

BBC

Possible Vacancies in 2009

- Engineering
- Finance
- General Management
- IT
- Law
- Marketing
- Media
- Research & Development

Starting salary for 2009
£Competitive

Universities that the BBC plans to visit in 2008-9
Please check with your university careers service for details of events.

Application deadline
Year-round recruitment

Contact Details
✉ hr@bbchrdirect.co.uk
☎ 0370 333 1330

Turn to page 256 now to request more information or visit our new website at www.top100graduateemployers.com

The BBC is the world's best-known broadcasting brand with a remit to inform, educate and entertain. Today's digital BBC aims to engender creativity and trust, enriching people's lives with quality programming and services. BBC content is watched and listened to via eight national television channels, 10 national and 45 nations & regions radio stations, and can be accessed online.

The BBC's Royal Charter defines expectations of the corporation in a digital, on-demand world; the emphasis changing from a one-way, studio-based broadcaster of programmes, into an audience focused 'anytime, anywhere, anyhow', content brand. Recent changes such as the launches of iPlayer, strengthen this directional shift.

The work environment couldn't be further removed from the standard nine to five. The BBC is creating an environment that's friendly, welcoming and open to change. One that's as diverse as it is fast-moving, and where challenge and reward go hand-in-hand. The hours are variable and the dress code relaxed. But they are serious about what they do, and to join them successful applicants need to be passionate about their work. One of the rewards for such commitment is the BBC's keen attention to staff development.

Although there are advertised training schemes, most graduates tend to enter the BBC through one off vacancies advertised throughout the year rarely if ever mentioning a degree as a pre-requisite.

Everyone wants to find an inspirational place where they'll be encouraged to do things differently. Visit bbc.co.uk/jobs to find out more about the roles and what it takes to succeed there.

Bloomberg

Vacancies for around 200 graduates in 2009

- Finance
- IT
- Media
- Research & Development
- Sales

Vacancies also available in Asia and the USA.

Starting salary for 2009
£Competitive

Universities Bloomberg plans to visit in 2008-9
Please check with your university careers service for details of events.

Application deadline
Year-round recruitment

Contact Details
Turn to page 256 now to request more information or visit our new website at www.top100graduateemployers.com

Bloomberg is the leading global provider of data, news and analytics. The Bloomberg Professional® service and Bloomberg's media services provide real-time and archived financial and market data, pricing, trading, news and communications tools in a single, integrated package.

Bloomberg's clients include corporations, news organisations, financial and legal professionals, and individuals around the world. With over 10,000 employees operating in more than 127 countries, Bloomberg is truly international. The largest offices include New York, London and Tokyo, and this is where the majority of graduate opportunities are located.

Graduate positions include financial sales, software development, global data, IT, project management, news and many more. For most roles, a second language is desirable but not essential. Bloomberg recruits all year round and from any discipline. A passion for finance, technology or an international career is required. Bloomberg breaks down barriers between people and encourages communication by bringing colleagues together. With no job titles or executive areas, the culture fosters interaction at every level.

Bloomberg supports community programmes by reinvesting resources back into the society through sponsorships and employee volunteer activities. But the real depth and diversity of Bloomberg's way of life comes from the creativity and commitment of its people. Training is extensive and ongoing via Bloomberg University. Courses are wide-ranging and available to all, allowing graduates to progress quickly and take on real responsibility quickly. Opportunities are listed on the website and start dates are available throughout the year.

Bloomberg

MOVE THE MARKETS.
Reach out to the world.

Join the company at the forefront of finance and technology.

Bloomberg provides information to business leaders around the world. Our employees have a passion for excellence, no matter what their experience is. We foster that passion and encourage growth and development in every way possible. **Join Bloomberg.**

careers.bloomberg.com

graduates.bnpparibas.com

Vacancies for around 500 graduates in 2009

■ Investment Banking
■ IT

Vacancies also available in Europe, Asia, the USA and elsewhere in the world.

Starting salary for 2009
£Competitive

Universities BNP Paribas plans to visit in 2008-9
Bath, Bristol, Cambridge, Durham, Leeds, London, Manchester, Nottingham, Nottingham Trent, Oxford, Reading, Warwick, York
Please check with your university careers service for details of events.

Application deadline
See website for full details.

Contact Details
 bnpgrad09@alexmann.com
☎ 01344 747669
Turn to page 256 now to request more information or visit our new website at www.top100graduateemployers.com

BNP Paribas is a global leader in banking and financial services, ranking amongst the world's top five banks by market capitalisation and total assets, and one of only four banks globally with a AA+ or higher credit rating from Standard & Poor's. With over 160,000 employees in 85 countries, BNP Paribas offers truly global career opportunities.

BNP Paribas's Corporate and Investment Banking (CIB) division has built an enviable position in the banking world through its strong risk management, healthy balance sheet and world-leading expertise in derivatives and structured products. These qualities have enabled the firm to continue growing its global network and client base, even in the face of difficult market conditions.

Committed to early and rapid career development, BNP Paribas hires graduates directly into full-time positions rather than onto a rotational training programme. As well as first-class training, graduates benefit from on-the-job coaching and support from sector-leading professionals and have the advantage of putting what they learn into practice from the outset. With the freedom and encouragement to think creatively, and an environment that is both collaborative and nurturing, graduates learn fast from their experience and rapidly take on new responsibilities. It's a fast-track into a long-term career in the markets.

For bright, entrepreneurially minded individuals with excellent quantitative skills and the ability to quickly understand complex financial concepts, there are graduate and internship positions across all business areas of BNP Paribas CIB and throughout its global network of offices.

LOVE MODELS

WHEN YOU HEAR SOPHISTICATED MODELS, DO YOU THINK OF ADVANCED MATHEMATICAL STRATEGIES FOR IMPROVING TRADING PERFORMANCE?

We do. Our focus on providing our clients with technically sophisticated, bespoke banking solutions has helped us grow into one of the world's leading investment banks. And our strong balance sheet and rigorous risk management* has us well placed for the future – but what will drive our ongoing success and define our appeal to clients in new and expanding markets?

The answer is simple – ideas. Having the vision and confidence to invest in ideas, and the patience to let them flourish is what will make a great firm even better. That's why, even in the face of difficult market conditions, we're still growing, still innovating and still looking for people like you to make us even better. If you are looking for a career that truly values creative thinking, quantitative ability and entrepreneurial spirit, then invest in a career with BNP Paribas.

*One of only four banks worldwide to be rated AA+ by Standard & Poor's

Investing in ideas
graduates.bnpparibas.com

BNP PARIBAS
CORPORATE & INVESTMENT BANKING

BCG

THE BOSTON CONSULTING GROUP

www.bcg.com

**Vacancies for around
30 graduates in 2009**

■ Consulting

Vacancies also available in Europe,
Asia, the USA and elsewhere in
the world.

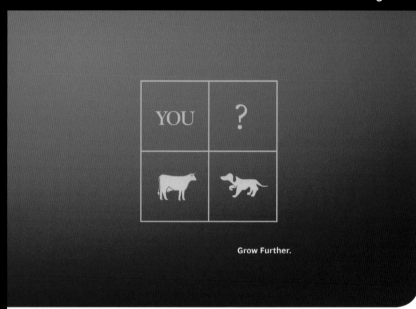

YOU ?

Grow Further.

Starting salary for 2009
£Competitive

**Universities that
Boston Consulting Group
plans to visit in 2008-9**
Cambridge, Dublin, Durham,
Edinburgh, Glasgow,
London, Oxford
Please check with your university
careers service for details of events.

Application deadline
7th November 2008

Contact Details
✉ lonrecruiting@bcg.com
☎ 020 7753 5666

Turn to page 256 now to request more
information or visit our new website at
www.top100graduateemployers.com

The Boston Consulting Group (BCG) is a global management consulting firm and the world's leading advisor on business strategy. BCG help their clients achieve sustainable competitive advantage, build more capable organisations and secure lasting results. BCG continues to experience unprecedented growth and is seeking highly talented graduates to join their world class team and drive this momentum forward.

New joiners can make a difference at BCG. They will collaborate daily with the world's leading businesses on a wide range of high-level strategic challenges. As a member of a team, their role will be to partner with clients in all sectors and regions to identify their highest-value opportunities, address their most critical challenges and transform their businesses. They will drive client results, helping leaders in business not just play better, but change the rules of the game.

BCG cares about personal growth. BCG employees can be sponsored through an MBA in a leading business school, choose a secondment with a world-class client or work in one of our many offices around the world. BCG's career development team offers their employees the opportunity to be mentored, stretched and intellectually challenged. BCG's international training programme will also help one develop a comprehensive toolkit of business and management skills that will provide the springboard to excel in any field within BCG or beyond.

At BCG, graduates will find a career of challenge and reward. Since 1990 BCG has grown at an industry beating 16% annually. This record growth creates expansive opportunity for their employees: broader choices, faster learning, and rapid advancement. BCG is looking for people to join and continue this success.

Grow Further.

At BCG, your potential is limited only by your talents and ambitions. You will work daily with the world's leading businesses on a wide range of high-level strategic challenges. The knowledge, experience, and skills you'll gain will provide the springboard you need to excel in any field within BCG or beyond.

How far will you grow?

THE BOSTON CONSULTING GROUP

bp

beyond petroleum

Vacancies for around
150+ graduates in 2009

- Accountancy
- Engineering
- Finance
- Logistics

Starting salary for 2009
£30,000+

Universities that BP plans to visit in 2008-9
Bath, Birmingham, Cambridge, Leeds, London, Manchester, Nottingham, Oxford, Strathclyde
Please check with your university careers service for details of events.

Application deadline
See website for full details.

Contact Details
Turn to page 256 now to request more information or visit our new website at www.top100graduateemployers.com

Energy – possibly the most important commodity in the world today. But what is going to happen tomorrow? How can a growing global demand for energy be met without compromising the planet? BP is going further than ever before to discover new reserves, produce cleaner fuels and develop new energies, and investing in the technology and the people to do it.

BP explores, produces, refines, markets, trades and distributes energy, and it has 11 refineries around the world, 25,000 miles of pipeline and some of the world's leading brands – such as BP, Amoco and Castrol. Every day this global business produces about 3.8 million barrels of oil equivalent and serves some 15 million customers. Every year they invest more than $1 billion to technology and hire 750 graduates and interns to become the managers and technical experts of the future.

The next big idea? The next important breakthrough? It's there to be made.

BP recruits into three key disciplines – Engineering, Science or Business. Within each of these, there is a wide range of opportunities – from chemical engineering to geoscience, chemistry to finance, trading to civil engineering. Graduates are based in Exploration & Production, Refining & Marketing, Alternative Energy or within the corporate team. But no matter where they work, they need the drive, ambition, business and analytical skills, and flexibility to succeed.

Deeper water. Remoter places. Cleaner fuels. New processes. Faster technology. Change thinking. BP is going there and beyond.

10 miles down through sea, salt, rock and millions of years.

We're going there and beyond.

Careers in Engineering, Science & Business

We are going to previously inaccessible places to find the energy that the world depends on today and in the future. The Atlantis platform in the Gulf of Mexico is the deepest moored floating oil and gas production facility in the world. This 58,700 metric ton semi-submersible platform has over 18 wells and a mobile drilling unit that enables us to get to previously unreachable energy reservoirs. Where will we go next? You tell us. Look beyond the limits.

BP is an equal opportunity employer.

bp

beyond petroleum

www.bp.com/ukgraduates

BRITISH AIRWAYS

ba.com/careers

**Vacancies for around
30 graduates in 2009**

- Engineering
- Finance
- General Management
- Human Resources
- IT
- Purchasing

Starting salary for 2009
£22,500

**Universities that
British Airways
plans to visit in 2008-9**
Please check with your university
careers service for details of events.

Application deadline
Varies by function
See website for full details.

Contact Details
Turn to page 256 now to request more
information or visit our new website at
www.top100graduateemployers.com

British Airways is the UK's largest international airline and each
year flies more than 33 million customers to 550 destinations
worldwide. It employs around 43,000 staff, mainly in the UK,
and the company's 245-strong fleet of aircraft make an average
of 800 flights every day.

The excitement and challenges of the airline industry has long made British
Airways a popular choice for graduates and the company currently offers five
different entry-level training schemes.

The 'Leaders for Business' programme is designed to equip high-flying
individuals with a wide range of management and customer service skills that
they can apply anywhere across the company. This demanding programme
lasts a maximum of three years and includes a series of placements within
different parts of the organisation.

For those interested in a role in finance & procurement, human resources
or IT, British Airways offers a professional development programme in
each area. Where appropriate, graduates are sponsored to attain a
relevant qualification such as CIMA, CIPS or ACCA. There are also
opportunities in operational research and within the airline's engineering
department for graduates with a degree in aeronautical, mechanical or
electrical engineering.

The minimum entry requirement for all British Airways' graduate programmes
is a 2.1 degree and applicants must have the right to live and work in the UK.

British Airways' headquarters is at Waterside, close to Heathrow Airport
and many new graduates are based in or around the Heathrow area.

www.bt.com/grads

Vacancies for around 250 graduates in 2009

- Accountancy
- Consulting
- Engineering
- Finance
- General Management
- Human Resources
- IT
- Law
- Marketing
- Media
- Purchasing
- Sales

Starting salary for 2009
£27,000+

Universities that BT plans to visit in 2008-9

Aston, Bath, Belfast, Birmingham, Cambridge, Cardiff, Dublin, Durham, Edinburgh, Lancaster, Leeds, Loughborough, Manchester, Newcastle, Nottingham, Oxford, Sheffield, Southampton, Ulster, Warwick, York
Please check with your university careers service for details of events.

Application deadline
See website for full details.

Contact Details
Turn to page 256 now to request more information or visit our new website at www.top100graduateemployers.com

↘ find out more www.bt.com/grads

BT is leading the way in IT and telecoms services. It works with some of the world's most admired companies, influencing how they do business in over 170 countries and across five continents. BT is widely admired for putting corporate social responsibility at the centre of everything it does.

BT offers three different career paths or 'streams' within its graduate development programme: the Professional Services and Customer Experience stream offers a range of business focused roles including project management, management consultancy and sales, and provides a real understanding of how important it is to put customers at the heart of any business. The ICT stream offers roles ranging from IT Systems Analyst to Network Security to Software and Platform Engineering. The Functional Specialists stream includes roles in HR, Marketing, Finance, Procurement and Supply Chain and Law. Each of these roles lead to professional qualifications.

BT's graduate programme focuses on the development of core skills, leadership capabilities and potential through structured development and coaching. The programme also lets graduates specialise in areas which suit their strengths and chosen career path and provides opportunities to advance quickly, make a difference, and shoulder real responsibility from day one.

Graduates will need at least 280 UCAS points, a 2.1 Honours Degree, or international equivalent in any degree discipline. Benefits include a highly competitive starting salary from £27,000 with an annual performance based bonus, a sign-on bonus, share and profit-sharing schemes, company contributory pension plan and 27.5 days annual leave. BT is an equal opportunities employer.

Explore a world of technology/ Uncover your hidden talents/ Learn how businesses really work/Reveal what it takes to motivate people/

What's your calling?:

ICT

Professional Services

& Customer Experience

Finance, HR, Law, Marketing

Procurement & Supply Chain

Whether it's working alongside major global customers delivering communications and IT solutions, bringing Broadband to remote areas or delivering flexible digital TV on demand, we're changing the way people work and live. That means wherever you want your career to go, BT can take it.

We've designed a development programme that fits around you and gets you to the heart of the action from day one. It's our aim to create tomorrow's BT leaders– the business people, technologists and visionaries who'll shape all of our futures. You won't be alone either – you'll be joining a talented graduate community that's over 400 strong.

Visit our website to find out more about our graduate opportunities.

www.bt.com/grads

Cadbury

Vacancies for around 18 graduates in 2009

- Engineering
- Finance
- IT
- Logistics
- Manufacturing
- Marketing
- Purchasing
- Research & Development
- Sales

Starting salary for 2009
£26,000
Plus £2,000 joining bonus.

Universities that Cadbury plans to visit in 2008-9
Aston, Bath, Birmingham, Leeds, London, Loughborough, Manchester, Nottingham, Reading, Sheffield, Surrey
Please check with your university careers service for details of events.

Application deadline
See website for full details.

Contact Details
✉ cadburygraduates@csplc.com
☎ 0121 787 2437

Turn to page 256 now to request more information or visit our new website at www.top100graduateemployers.com

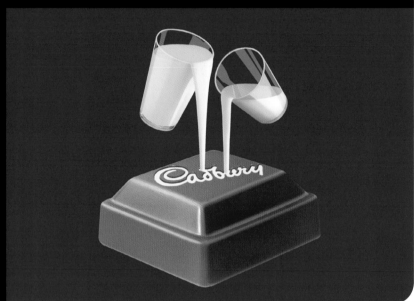

Cadbury needs little introduction. Its passion for quality and innovation has created brands that are known – and loved – by millions. Who else could excite the world with products as huge as Creme Egg, Trident and Dairy Milk? Of course, such brands aren't built without dedication; such global success doesn't happen without inspired commercial thinking. But these are qualities Cadbury insists on, and it's what they look for in their graduates.

Only a small number are talented enough to get their chance with Cadbury. But those lucky few get unprecedented experience across each area of the business as well as priceless support from their mentor and colleagues, all passionate about what they do. What's more, graduates get to work on real projects, in a real role, right from day one: what better way to start on the path that might lead them to become a future leader at Cadbury? Graduates will also be encouraged to create and run an exciting community-focused project together. This might be local or abroad – the only condition is that it brings to life Cadbury's spirit of Corporate Social Responsibility.

Many of Cadbury's business leaders started their careers on this scheme. Graduates with drive, enthusiasm and tenacity can achieve a great deal as they help Cadbury remain one of the biggest and best confectionery companies in the world. In return, great benefits are on offer as they'd expect from a blue chip FTSE 100 Company and the chance to build an exciting and irresistible future.

To find out more about careers with Cadbury – or industrial placement opportunities – visit www.cadburygraduates.co.uk

irresistible

If you think our products are tempting, take a close look at a Cadbury career. As one of the world's leading confectionery companies, there's only one way we can go – onwards and upwards. That's the attitude that inspires us to keep getting bigger and better, strengthening our brands and extending our leadership. As one of our leaders of tomorrow, you'll have real responsibility in a real job from day one, teaming up with like-minded people who inspire each other to achieve great things. From finance to engineering, from marketing to research, we want the best talent in every area of the business. Do you have the ambition, the acumen and the absolute commitment that will make you an irresistible choice?

YOU'LL REALLY WANT THIS
www.cadburygraduates.co.uk

CANCER RESEARCH UK

graduates.cancerresearchuk.org

Vacancies for around 100+ graduates in 2009

- Accountancy
- Consulting
- Finance
- General Management
- Human Resources
- IT
- Law
- Marketing
- Purchasing
- Research & Development
- Retailing

Starting salary for 2009
£Competitive

Universities that Cancer Research UK plans to visit in 2008-9
Bath, Cambridge, Edinburgh, Lancaster, London, Oxford, Warwick, York
Please check with your university careers service for details of events.

Application deadline
See website for full details.

Contact Details
Turn to page 256 now to request more information or visit our new website at www.top100graduateemployers.com

Cancer Research UK is the world's leading independent organisation dedicated to cancer research. Over 3,000 of the world's best doctors, nurses and scientific staff work on their pioneering research. But equally important are the dedicated individuals in fundraising, marketing, HR, communications, IT, finance and other support functions.

Their total annual income is around £470 million – an achievement that underlines the business expertise, commercial vision and marketing talent that supports the groundbreaking research work at their world-class centre of scientific excellence. So wherever graduates join them they can expect to make a real contribution from day one. And to help successful applicants achieve their own ambitions, they will benefit from a unique combination of on-the-job learning and formal, professional training.

Clearly, a career with Cancer Research UK offers plenty in the way of personal fulfilment. But what many people overlook is how commercially challenging and professionally rewarding their work can be. So while empathy for the cause is important, above all they're looking for ambitious, business-minded graduates who can help drive the organisation forward in the months and years to come.

Every year, Cancer Research UK offers a variety of graduate opportunities in all aspects of their work, including fundraising, science and corporate support services. To find out more about specific opportunities, visit their website.

Graduates can also sign up for email alerts which will keep them up to date with vacancies at http://jobs.cancerresearchuk.org/alerts_signup_form.php

Like you, we plan to go on learning.

It's a fact that more and more graduates are actively seeking a different job with better opportunities to learn and progress. This just shows the importance of finding a career that will stretch you. Happily, that's exactly what we can offer you.

When you join one of our programmes, you'll start a high-level career at the forefront of your field. Not only will you benefit from a unique combination of on-the-job learning and comprehensive training, but you'll also be making a difference to thousands of cancer sufferers and their families. How many graduates can say that?

Start by visiting
http://graduates.cancerresearchuk.org/

JOIN THE DOTS

CANCER RESEARCH UK

Dreams. Realities.

In an increasingly complex world, everyone has different ambitions. Individuals strive to pursue personal goals. Business owners try to secure loans to fund their vision. Governments invest in alternative energies. Corporations grow, merge and develop. Every day, the world is being shaped and enhanced as people pursue their dreams. As the pre-eminent global financial services company, Citi is committed to turning these dreams into realities.

As a result, Citi's 200 million clients enjoy having the backing not just to reach their goals, but to surpass them. Likewise, Citi's people – who are right at the centre of global financial services – enjoy unrivalled opportunities to progress within wide-ranging operations spanning 100 countries.

This has always been the way Citi does business: with a pioneering spirit that fuelled its beginnings in New York in 1812 to becoming the global leader it is today. Continually pushing boundaries, entering markets like Dubai and Pakistan before they emerged, Citi shapes the future of financial services perhaps more than any other company. Today, more than ever, this innovation continues as Citi breaks new ground across the banking industry and beyond.

All of which means Analysts could be part of a global environment where opportunities open up career routes far beyond their expectations. Whichever business group is joined, Citi invests heavily in career-long learning initiatives and tailored development programmes. So, Citi people do more than achieve their ambitions. They exceed them.

YOUR FUTURE NEVER SLEEPS.

Dreams.   **Realities.**

After a fruitful strategy session with a local Hong Kong designer, Fiona joins her Citi colleagues for a late dinner in Kowloon. >>> But in Dubai, Clark is busy discussing a bond issue with the Minister of Finance. >>> In Paris, Fareed smiles as his thrilled client credits him with a successful public launch. >>> And in New York, Sarah checks how today's increase in oil prices has affected the Hang Seng.

Around the world and around the clock, Citi employees are doing some of the most exciting and challenging work in the finance sector. It's a background that allows our people to go on to run everything from global companies to entire countries. The opportunities are out there if you know where to look. A good place to start is oncampus.citi.com

Citi never sleeps℠

www.faststream.gov.uk

**Vacancies for around
500 graduates in 2009**

- Engineering
- Finance
- General Management
- IT
- Purchasing

**Starting salary for 2009
Up to £27,000**

**Universities that the
Fast Stream
plans to visit in 2008-9**

Aberystwyth, Birmingham,
Durham, East Anglia,
Lancaster, Liverpool,
London, Nottingham,
Oxford, Oxford Brookes,
Sheffield, Sussex, Warwick
Please check with your university
careers service for details of events.

**Application deadline
30th November 2008**
See website for full details.

Contact Details
✉ faststream@parity.net
☎ 01276 400333

Turn to page 256 now to request more
information or visit our new website at
www.top100graduateemployers.com

WHERE WILL YOUR IDEAS END UP?

Education. Health. Defence. Transport. Climate change. International development. These are just some of the areas where graduates on the Civil Service Fast Stream get to put their ideas into practice, as they work on issues that affect the entire country and beyond.

The Civil Service Fast Stream is an accelerated development programme aimed at people who have the potential to become the Civil Service leaders of tomorrow. As such, Fast Streamers are given considerable early responsibility and, from the outset, move regularly between projects to gain a range of experiences and skills.

They are exposed to three distinct but complementary professional areas: policy delivery, operational delivery and corporate services. This gives them a wide understanding of how government delivers public service.

As part of their development, graduates also enjoy a mixture of on-the-job training and formal courses, as well as receiving ongoing feedback on their performance.

So what qualities are needed to make it to the top? Lucidity, confidence, articulacy and decisiveness are all important, as is an analytical and open-minded approach. Graduates must have a minimum 2:2 in any discipline. Above all, they need to be the kind of people who can deliver results, and who are excited by the idea of making a positive and highly visible impact across many different areas of society.

There are many opportunities available, including schemes for economists, statisticians and technology in business. For other Civil Service opportunities, visit www.careers.civil-service.gov.uk

SOME OF YOUR IDEAS WILL BE SAVED FOR AN EMERGENCY.

Others might end up in classrooms. In hospitals. As part of the transport network.
Or, occasionally, on the six o'clock news. One thing's for certain. Every different
area you work in (and there will be many), you'll be finding solutions to some of
society's most important issues. Some of which need answering right away.

faststream.gov.uk

CIVIL SERVICE
FAST STREAM

CLIFFORD CHANCE

**Vacancies for around
130 graduates in 2009**
For training contracts starting in 2011

■ Law

Starting salary for 2009
£37,400

**Universities that
Clifford Chance
plans to visit in 2008-9**
Aberdeen, Belfast, Bristol,
Cambridge, Durham,
Edinburgh, Exeter, Glasgow,
Leeds, London, Manchester,
Nottingham, Oxford,
Southampton, St Andrews,
Warwick, York
Please check with your university
careers service for details of events.

Application deadline
See website for full details.

Contact Details
✉ recruitment.london@
cliffordchance.com
☎ 020 7006 3003

Turn to page 256 now to request more
information or visit our new website at
www.top100graduateemployers.com

Clifford Chance is a leading international law firm delivering
innovative and practical legal solutions to corporate, institutional,
government and private clients around the world. The firm's rapid
expansion following some ground-breaking mergers has fostered
a culture that is pioneering and entrepreneurial, flexible and open,
and which emphasises the fundamental importance of teamwork
and of providing rich career opportunities for its people.

Clifford Chance's global network provides the firm's clients with local expertise
in all major markets and offers trainees and lawyers excellent opportunities
for international exposure. Most transactions and client matters have an
international dimension but Clifford Chance takes this a step further, offering
the very real prospect of overseas placements and secondments.

The firm's scale and reach across six sector-leading practices – Corporate,
Capital Markets, Banking & Finance, Real Estate, Litigation & Dispute Resolution,
and Tax, Pensions and Employment – underpinned by its reputation for
excellence, ensures a steady flow of stimulating and challenging assignments,
while the firm's commitment to career development and its first-class lawyer-
support resources mean that trainees take responsibility for substantive work as
early as possible.

Trainees at Clifford Chance can look forward to learning about business and
law in a diverse and supportive environment, and exposure to the deals and
clients that populate the business headlines. In addition, the firm's commitment
to an extensive programme of pro bono and community projects further adds
to the breadth of opportunity, enabling lawyers to use their skills and business
experience in other fields and develop truly rewarding legal careers.

it's WE not ME

At Clifford Chance it is our people and their ability to work creatively together that drive our success and enable us to attract challenging and stimulating work around the world.

We have established an enviable reputation as a leader and a first mover, meeting the needs of increasingly global markets, building top-tier practices in every key area of business law, and reaching out through an international network that spans the Americas, Asia, the Middle East and Europe. At the same time our rapid growth has fostered a pioneering, entrepreneurial spirit that encourages our people to be both bold and innovative, and a culture that emphasises the fundamental importance of teamwork and collaboration across practice areas and jurisdictions.

From exposure to the highest quality work and headline-making deals to the breadth of our pro bono and community programmes we offer the prospect of an outstanding legal career. Joining us as a trainee, you'll play an important role in international teams comprising people from diverse backgrounds and cultures and, like nearly 80% of our trainees, you could spend six months of your training in one of our overseas offices. With close support and first-class resources we'll help you to build a truly rewarding and long-term career in law.

To discover more about our graduate and vacation placement opportunities visit
www.cliffordchance.com/gradsuk

CLIFFORD
CHANCE

www.cliffordchance.com/gradsuk

C/M/S/

www.cmstalklaw.com

Vacancies for around 60 graduates in 2009
For training contracts starting in 2011

■ Law

Starting salary for 2009
£37,500

Universities that CMS Cameron McKenna plans to visit in 2008-9
Aberdeen, Birmingham, Bristol, Cambridge, Cardiff, Durham, Edinburgh, Exeter, Glasgow, Leeds, Leicester, Liverpool, London, Manchester, Nottingham, Oxford, Sheffield, Strathclyde, Warwick, York
Please check with your university careers service for details of events.

Application deadline
31st July 2009

Contact Details

✉ gradrec@cms-cmck.com

☎ 0845 300 0491

Turn to page 256 now to request more information or visit our new website at www.top100graduateemployers.com

CMS is the leading organisation of European law firms which includes CMS Cameron McKenna, a firm famed for being a client-focused law firm with excellent training and overseas opportunities.

Trainee solicitors are being recruited for their London, Bristol and Scottish offices. Training contracts will have four six-month seats, gaining experience in various practice areas: Banking and International Finance; Commercial; Corporate; Energy, Projects and Construction; Insurance and Reinsurance; and Real Estate. Working alongside this traditional Practice Group structure the firm also uses Sector Groups to build teams taking an industry, rather than a purely legal, perspective, allowing for sector expertise and tailored advice.

There will be plenty of opportunity to try new things in each seat including client secondments, regional office secondments or time in one of their renowned European offices such as Bulgaria, the Czech Republic, Hungary, Poland, Romania, Russia and Ukraine. Having been voted 'Central and Eastern Europe Law Firm of the Year 2007' (PLC Which Law) the latter is particularly encouraged to ensure trainees develop their skills and knowledge to the best of their abilities.

For undergraduates the firm offers the opportunity to spend two weeks at CMS Cameron McKenna in London, Bristol and Scotland to gain an insight into the 'life of a trainee solicitor'. These schemes run over Christmas, Easter and summer, and are open to anyone interested in pursuing a legal career.

The firm will cover fees for the GDL and LPC and provide successful applicants with a maintenance grant of up to £7,500.

The **co-operative**

**Vacancies for around
12 graduates in 2009**

■ **Finance**

■ **General Management**

Starting salary for 2009
£Competitive

**Universities that
The Co-operative Group
plans to visit in 2008-9**

Cambridge, Lancaster,
Leeds, Liverpool,
Manchester, Oxford,
Sheffield, Warwick
Please check with your university
careers service for details of events.

Application deadline
July 2009

Contact Details
✉ **graduate.recruitment@
co-op.co.uk**

Turn to page 256 now to request more
information or visit our new website at
www.top100graduateemployers.com

The **co-operative** 4,000 of our outlets
are powered by renewable energy.

With 16 different businesses, 4,500 outlets and 73,000 people,
The Co-operative Group isn't just a food retailer but also a
travel provider, a funeral director, a pharmacist, a legal services
provider, and much more. But the real difference lies not just in
what they do; it's what they are – a co-operative (and the world's
largest consumer co-operative at that).

Unlike a plc, they do not just exist to make profit. Everything they do is for the
benefit of their members and the community as a whole. They are driven by
their social goals and their co-operative values give them a positive advantage
– for instance, they already sell more Fairtrade products than any other retailer.

But that doesn't mean they are any less ambitious – they still offer the depth and
breadth of challenge you'd expect from a commercially focussed business.

For those who want to pursue a rewarding career without compromising their
values, the Group offers two programmes: Business Management and Finance.

On the Business Management programme, rather than simply rotating
from function to function, graduates choose from a wide range of business
critical projects ensuring the entire experience meets their career aspirations.
Alternatively, for those with a passion for finance, graduates might want to
consider their CIMA accredited programme. This offers four nine-month
placements, where graduates gain specialist knowledge in functions ranging
from internal audit to tax.

Either way, graduates will gain experience across a number of different
businesses and enjoy all the support they'll need to drive their own career both
professionally and personally.

The **co-operative**

We're **a £9 billion business**
We're **4.5 million members**
We're **73,000 colleagues**
We're **4,500 outlets**
We're **one unique graduate employer**

Business Management or Finance Graduate Programme

As the world's largest consumer co-operative we can offer you a graduate experience that is altogether different. Our 16 different businesses – that vary from food to pharmacy, and from funerals to travel – will all be vying for your talents. Choosing the business critical projects that you work on, you'll ensure that the entire experience meets your career ambitions. But the real difference is, you'll be part of a co-operative. This means you'll be joining a business that's as ethically minded as it is commercially focused – perfect if you want to achieve your goals without compromising your values.

Discover our graduates' **altogether**|different
experiences at www.altogetherdifferent.com

corus

**Vacancies for around
150 graduates in 2009**

Engineering

Finance

Human Resources

IT

Logistics

Manufacturing

Purchasing

Research & Development

Sales

Starting salary for 2009
£Competitive

**Universities that Corus
plans to visit in 2008-9**
Aston, Bath, Birmingham,
Bristol, Cambridge, Cardiff,
Durham, Lancaster, Leeds,
Leicester, Liverpool,
London, Loughborough,
Manchester, Newcastle,
Northumbria, Nottingham,
Oxford, Sheffield,
Southampton, Strathclyde,
Swansea, Warwick
Please check with your university
careers service for details of events.

Application deadline
See website for full details.

Contact Details
✉ recruitment@corusgroup.com
☎ 01926 488025

Turn to page 256 now to request more
information or visit our new website at
www.top100graduateemployers.com

Imagine what the world would be like without steel. No hospitals, schools, transportation systems, even paperclips; the list is endless! Corus is a subsidiary of Tata Steel, the world's sixth largest and second most global steel producer, with a combined presence in nearly 50 countries.

Corus metal is used globally in projects such as the new Grand Theatre in Beijing and at Ground Zero in New York; closer to home it is used for 80% of UK made cars, track for the London Underground and the Emirates Stadium, London.

Corus is passionate about making the world a better place and is committed to the adoption of sustainable practices. Using the perfect blend of world-class manufacturing processes, innovative research centres and inspired individuals; Corus can achieve the vision of becoming leaders in their field.

To achieve this vision, people with qualities that will fit into the Corus way of thinking are essential; these include passion, drive, enthusiasm, imagination and the ability to adapt to new challenges. Corus look for innovative minds and skills that go beyond just pure academic ability in order to drive change and really make a difference

Corus has the size and diversity to tailor careers by providing real life projects from the outset and challenges that will be interesting, dynamic and relevant. Those entering the Corus Graduate Scheme will receive on the job and formal training (including Professional Accreditation) designed to develop management and technical skills.

6A

Triumph Bonneville T100

CF85.430

	428
	12,600
	24
	7t
	44t
	Corus

corus

1C

Bugatti Veyron

	100
	67
	365
	ltrs
	kg

2B

Airbus A380

4F

Delhi Metro

	254
	987
mph	7,993
hp	64
cc	1.9t
cylinders	
weight	Corus
steel expertise	

passengers	555
mph	560
fuel capacity	310,000ltrs
wing span	79.5m
height	277t
steel expertise	Corus

5D

HMS Queen Elizabeth

Top Careers

When it comes to taking your career forward, Corus is the driving force.

displacement	
length	65,000t
range	274m
crew	18,520km
aircraft	1,450
steel expertise	48
	Corus

We are passionate about making the world a better place. Using the perfect blend of world-class manufacturing processes, innovative research centres and inspired individuals, we can achieve the vision of becoming leaders in our field.

If you take pride in everything you do and strive to be the best, go to our website to find out more. All applications are on-line.

www.corusgroupcareers.com

Corus is now part of Tata Steel **TATA** STEEL

CREDIT SUISSE

www.credit-suisse.com/careers

Vacancies for around 200 graduates in 2009

- Finance
- Investment Banking
- IT

Starting salary for 2009
£Competitive

Universities Credit Suisse plans to visit in 2008-9
Cambridge, City,
London, Manchester,
Oxford, Warwick
Please check with your university
careers service for details of events.

Application deadline
21st November 2008
See website for full details.

Contact Details
Turn to page 256 now to request more
information or visit our new website at
www.top100graduateemployers.com

Credit Suisse provides investment banking, private banking and asset management services to clients across the world. Active in over fifty countries and employing more than 45,000 people, Credit Suisse is one of the world's premier banks.

Credit Suisse offers intellectual challenges, high rewards and global development potential for individuals who share an enthusiasm for business-critical innovation. There are opportunities in Private Banking, Investment Banking (including fixed income and equities), Asset Management, Information Technology, Operations and other support functions, as well as a range of internships and placement programmes.

There are exceptional opportunities for growth in new product areas and emerging markets; there are equally exceptional opportunities for the people who can deliver that growth.

Credit Suisse's training programmes are designed to be best in class. Content varies among business areas, but all programmes combine formal learning with on-the-job practice and personal coaching to create an environment for further development. And, their award-winning Business School encourages learning and growth throughout one's career.

It's not easy choosing the right career – or the right place to start that career – but after spending a little time exploring, the decision gets easier. Most people who join Credit Suisse do so because of 'the people'. Credit Suisse appeals to intelligent and outgoing personalities who want to work together in an atmosphere of co-operation and respect. It's a different perspective on how a big bank should go about its business, but it works for Credit Suisse.

Some think
one point of view.

**We think
thousands
of opinions.**

There's great strength in keeping an open mind. A great
wisdom to be had from sharing personal experience. And
that's why we trust our people to work more independently,
using their best judgement to innovate and influence our business.

Take a closer look at **www.credit-suisse.com/careers**

Thinking New Perspectives.

Vacancies for around 50 graduates in 2009

 IT

Vacancies also available in the USA.

Starting salary for 2009
£30,000

Data Connection is one of the world's leading communications and telephony technology companies. They are a dynamic, fast-moving company with offices in the UK, San Francisco and Washington DC. For the past five years, they have been placed in the top 15 of The Sunday Times '100 Best Companies to Work For'. Their current growth, huge future opportunities, and massive investment in new technology and people development means that there has never been a more exciting time to join them.

Universities that Data Connection plans to visit in 2008-9

Bath, Bristol, Cambridge, Durham, Edinburgh, London, Loughborough, Oxford, St Andrews, Warwick, York
Please check with your university careers service for details of events.

Established for over 26 years, they are a strategic technology supplier to both telephone service providers and computer manufacturers ranging from big names such as Microsoft, Cisco, BT and AT&T, to small providers and start-ups.

Graduates will start off in a technical role developing their world class products or supporting their customers. They can then continue to develop their career in software and hardware development and support, or move into project and people management, sales, marketing, or product management.

Successful applicants do not need prior computing experience. However, an enquiring mind and the proven ability to solve complex problems are essential. They should have an outstanding academic record: all A grades at A-Level (or equivalent) and a good degree. Allied with this, Data Connection looks for people with good communication skills and outstanding technical aptitude.

Application deadline
Year-round recruitment

Data Connection cares passionately about employee development and believes in taking talented individuals and working with them to fulfil their potential. Their culture is all about doing the difficult things very well – and that includes the way they manage and develop their people.

Contact Details

✉ recruit@dataconnection.com

☎ 020 8366 1177

Turn to page 256 now to request more information or visit our new website at www.top100graduateemployers.com

YOUR CAREER
YOUR CHOICES
YOUR COMPANY

Data Connection is one of the world's leading communications technology companies, with a customer base that includes Cisco, Microsoft, IBM, Ericsson and British Telecom. We recruit exceptionally bright and energetic graduates and postgraduates from **any degree discipline** – people with the ability and desire to tackle problems which would defeat the vast majority – and then train them to become world-class professionals and managers, across our engineering, support, product management, sales, and marketing organisations. For the past five years, we have been placed in the top 15 of the Sunday Times **'100 Best Companies to Work For'**. Our current growth, huge future opportunities, and massive investment in new technology and people development means that there has never been a more exciting time to join us.

Your Career. Join us and you will find that the focus is all about you. We provide you with the freedom, support and flexibility to drive your career in the direction that you choose. We invest heavily in personalised training – and offer one of the best benefits packages in the industry (our graduates start on a remuneration of **£35,000**).

Your Choices. What happens to you is determined by your own ability and desire. There are no rigid programmes, pre-set career paths, excessive hours, or unreasonable demands. You will work hard, but in a stimulating and supportive environment where you will be able to choose from a variety of **challenging opportunities**, working alongside some of the brightest minds in the country.

Your Company. It is your company in more ways than one. A substantial part of the company is owned by the Data Connection Employee Benefit Trust (EBT), which distributes a **share of profit** to all employees, equitably rewarding them for their contribution and encouraging long-term commitment. In addition, we also operate an employee **stock option plan**, which further provides ownership incentives to our people.

It's your decision. Take control of your career now, by visiting **www.dataconnection.com/careers**

Deloitte.

www.deloitte.co.uk/graduates

Vacancies for around 1,000 graduates in 2009

- Accountancy
- Consulting
- Finance
- IT

Starting salary for 2009
£Competitive

Universities that Deloitte plans to visit in 2008-9
Please check with your university careers service for details of events.

Application deadline
Year-round recruitment

Contact Details
Turn to page 256 now to request more information or visit our new website at www.top100graduateemployers.com

> Wouldn't you
> like to have it all?
> Don't let anyone ever
> tell you that you can't.

Deloitte's breadth and depth of service means they can offer graduates a wide range of career opportunities. Providing fully integrated advice across Audit, Tax, Consulting and Corporate Finance, Deloitte is a leading force in the professional services industry, with 150,000 people across the globe and 11,000 in the UK alone.

Working across all major industries, from Financial Services, Technology, Media & Telecommunications, through to Consumer Business and Travel & Tourism, Deloitte offers the kind of clients, complexity and challenges graduates need to continue their personal growth.

The professional services Deloitte provides are absolutely vital to their clients' businesses. The way they work is uniquely collaborative: by drawing on expertise from across the firm, Deloitte creates integrated teams to meet the full range of challenges their clients face.

The training and development programmes Deloitte provides are second to none. They nurture talent with programmes that are tailor-made for each individual. From the Summer Vacation Scheme to their Insight Days, there are many ways to find out what working with Deloitte is really like, even before graduation.

Deloitte believes in plain speaking, pragmatic thinking, delivering on their promises, and a good work-life balance. And whatever degree has been achieved, successful applicants will be working with the best in every field. All of which makes Deloitte's offices very special places to work.

Wouldn't you like to have it all?
Don't let anyone ever tell you that you can't.

Choosing where to launch your career is one of the most important decisions you'll ever make. So pick an organisation that offers you everything you deserve. We mean early responsibility. Dynamic training opportunities. Career progression. The chance to work successfully with a diverse range of clients in a collaborative culture. And in a firm that values its people and gives back to society.

The more you discover about us, the more you'll discover about yourself. So secure a place on our 2009 graduate programme now. Applications opened early this year and places are limited. Look out for big things on campus. It's your future. How far will you take it?

Discover more at **www.deloitte.co.uk/graduates**

Deutsche Bank /

www.db.com/careers

Vacancies for around 600 graduates in 2009

- Accountancy
- Finance
- Human Resources
- Investment Banking
- IT
- Law

Starting salary for 2009
£Competitive

Universities that Deutsche Bank plans to visit in 2008-9
Please check with your university careers service for details of events.

Application deadline
See website for full details.

Contact Details
Turn to page 256 now to request more information or visit our new website at www.top100graduateemployers.com

Deutsche Bank is committed to being the best financial services provider in the world. And, as an aspirational employer with the platform to lift careers to the next level, it fosters a diverse, inclusive work environment that encourages new ideas. It prides itself on building a long-term relationship with its employees.

The key to Deutsche Bank's success remains constant: a focus on client needs, a spirit of innovation, a broad range of expertise combined with technological power and financial strength delivered by diverse, highly-skilled professionals across the globe.

Deutsche Bank's drive to be the best financial services provider has gained it numerous accolades. In the past year it has been recognised as 'Bond and Derivatives house of the year', 'World's best risk management house' and 'World's best foreign exchange house', and in 2007 it swept the board at the Lipper and ISR Awards.

Deutsche Bank offers both comprehensive Analyst Internship and Training Programs which are designed to develop business and technical skills and provide graduates with the opportunity to excel in their new career, through on-the-job training, rotations and mentoring.

The organisation is continually visiting leading campuses around the world searching for talent and are looking for fresh ideas, innovative solutions and an entrepreneurial spirit.

Please visit www.db.com/careers to find out more.

**Your vision: To reach for the top.
Our promise: Lifting you even higher.**

You thrive on achievement and you want to see just how far your talent will take you. We do too. That's why, at Deutsche Bank, you'll be given the opportunity to realize your greatest ambitions. As one of the world's leading financial institutions, we have the platform to take your career higher. You will be part of an innovative, modern corporate culture that celebrates achievement.

Join us in: Asset Management – Finance – Global Banking – Global Markets – Human Resources – Operations – Private Wealth Management – Legal, Risk & Capital – Technology.

Expect the better career.

Find out more at **www.db.com/careers**

A Passion to Perform.   **Deutsche Bank** ◪

DLA PIPER

www.dlapiper.com

**Vacancies for around
100 graduates in 2009**
For training contracts starting in 2011

 Law

Starting salary for 2009
£Competitive

**Universities DLA Piper
plans to visit in 2008-9**
Aberdeen, Birmingham,
Bristol, Cambridge,
Cardiff, Dundee, Durham,
Edinburgh, Exeter, Glasgow,
Hull, Kent, Leeds, Leicester,
Liverpool, London,
Manchester, Newcastle,
Nottingham, Oxford,
Sheffield, St Andrews,
Strathclyde, Warwick, York
Please check with your university
careers service for details of events.

Application deadline
31st July 2009

Contact Details
 recruitment.graduate@
dlapiper.com
☎ 020 7796 6677
Turn to page 256 now to request more
information or visit our new website at
www.top100graduateemployers.com

With more than 3,700 lawyers across 25 countries throughout
Asia, Europe, the Middle East and the US, DLA Piper is
positioned to help companies with their legal needs anywhere
in the world.

Their current vision is to be the leading global business law firm.
Clients include some of the world's leading businesses, governments,
banks and financial institutions. DLA Piper offers trainees in all UK offices
the opportunity to apply for international secondments to their offices in
Abu Dhabi, Dubai, Moscow, Hong Kong, Singapore and Tokyo.

In 2008 DLA Piper won the prestigious National Graduate Recruitment Awards'
'Diversity Recruitment Award' proving their commitment to recruiting people
from a wide variety of backgrounds and ages.

There is no 'standard' DLA Piper trainee, however they do require a strong
academic background and look for good communicators and team players.
As well as this, in line with the firm's main focus of work, a keen interest in the
corporate world is essential – as is an appetite for life!

Trainees complete four six-month seats and progress is monitored through
regular reviews and feedback. The in-house Professional Skills Course
combined with high-quality on-the-job experience means an excellent
grounding on which DLA Piper's trainees build their professional careers.

The firm operates a formal summer scheme, which runs between June
and August each year. The schemes run for two weeks and allow a
thorough insight into DLA Piper. There are approximately 200 places
available nationwide.

BE LOCAL – GO GLOBAL

At DLA Piper, becoming the leading global business law firm depends on our most important asset – our people. That's why we take so much care in recruiting and retaining the best.

We offer exceptional worldwide career opportunities in a collaborative environment that is challenging, rewarding and truly different from that of our competitors. In the legal services sector, DLA Piper really is a different kind of business.

DLA Piper offers around 100 training contracts a year across our eight UK offices and our trainees have the opportunity to apply for secondments to our offices in Dubai, Hong Kong, Moscow, Singapore and Tokyo.

Our broad range of departments allow us to offer a diverse training contract, with our commitment to developing each trainee being paramount.

Approximately 200 summer scheme places are available each year allowing you to find out for yourself why we're different.

For more information visit: **www.dlapiper.com**

e·on

www.eon-uk.com/graduates

Vacancies for around 60 graduates in 2009

- Engineering
- Finance
- General Management
- Human Resources
- IT

Vacancies also available in Europe.

Starting salary for 2009
£25,000

Universities that E.ON plans to visit in 2008-9
Aberdeen, Aston, Bath, Belfast, Birmingham, Bristol, Cambridge, Cardiff, Durham, Edinburgh, Glasgow, Lancaster, Leeds, Leicester, Liverpool, London, Loughborough, Manchester, Nottingham, Oxford, Sheffield, Southampton, St Andrews, Strathclyde, Surrey, Warwick, York
Please check with your university careers service for details of events.

Application deadline
30th November 2008

Contact Details
✉ graduates@eonenquiries.com
☎ 0845 450 3395

Turn to page 256 now to request more information or visit our new website at www.top100graduateemployers.com

It's **amazing** to think that the work **I'm doing** today will play such an **important** part in **our future.**

John Batterham
E.ON Graduate

The energy industry is changing, and so are E.ON. From power plant to plug, the organisation is re-thinking the way their energy is generated, distributed and sold – paving the way for a better future.

This isn't just talk. As the world's largest investor-owned utility company and the UK's largest integrated energy company, E.ON are already one of the leading green generators with 21 wind farms around the UK and a newly completed biomass power station at Lockerbie. In fact their combined renewable portfolio generates enough green energy to power homes in a city the size of Manchester. So it's no wonder E.ON is leading the debate on climate change.

And it doesn't stop there. E.ON have the resources to really make a difference. In the next five years they are investing nearly £4 billion in generation – developing the latest technologies to reduce carbon emissions and improve energy efficiency. Successful applicants could be part of it.

Graduates with a passion about Changing Energy should join one of E.ON's graduate programmes in engineering, HR, IT, Finance or Corporate Management and they will not only get under the skin of the business, they will have the opportunity to build a great career.

By getting involved in large scale projects, gaining international exposure, managing personal development and gaining professional qualifications, successful applicants will make a positive impact on people's lives and the environment.

E.ON's ready for action, and so are its graduates.

Passion like **John's** is shaping
the **future of energy**

He's been making an impact from day one – reacting to incidents round the clock to help Central Networks keep the lights on in Nottinghamshire; developing innovative street lighting projects with a new Energy Services team; and getting to the heart of energy generation to understand the supply challenges he'll help us tackle in the future.

John's actions are making a positive difference. And yours could too.

Apply online at
eon-uk.com/graduates

Your energy shapes the future

ElI ERNST & YOUNG

Quality In Everything We Do

www.ey.com/uk/careers

Vacancies for around 750 graduates in 2009

- Accountancy
- Consulting
- Finance
- IT

Starting salary for 2009
£Competitive

Universities that Ernst & Young plans to visit in 2008-9

Aberdeen, Aston, Bath, Birmingham, Bristol, Brunel, Cambridge, Cardiff, Durham, Edinburgh, Essex, Exeter, Glasgow, Heriot-Watt, Lancaster, Leeds, Leicester, Liverpool, London, Loughborough, Manchester, Newcastle, Nottingham, Oxford, Reading, Sheffield, Southampton, St Andrews, Strathclyde, Warwick, York
Please check with your university careers service for details of events.

Application deadline
Year-round recruitment
See website for full details.

Contact Details

✉ gradrec@uk.ey.com

☎ 0800 289 208

Turn to page 256 now to request more information or visit our new website at www.top100graduateemployers.com

Ernst & Young makes a difference by helping its people, clients and wider communities achieve their potential. With 130,000 people in 700 locations across 140 countries, Ernst & Young helps clients with advisory, assurance, corporate finance and tax.

Graduates joining Ernst & Young in the UK deal with real business issues and challenges, building the relationships and expertise that help them develop, both personally and professionally, and that help their clients get the most from their businesses.

Everyone at the firm has access to an unparalleled breadth and depth of experience, including help from a counsellor and a mentor. Ernst & Young offers first rate training, early responsibility and opportunities to contribute, constant challenges, and projects to manage. In fact, graduates have everything they need to develop their career, but are also very much in charge of the direction it takes. Ernst & Young recently won the 'Best Training and Development' award in 'The Sunday Times 100 Best Companies to Work For' survey, and is confident that graduates receive the training they need to succeed.

Ernst & Young recognises that its clients prefer to engage with interesting people, and so thrives on the diversity of its individuals. Therefore, as long as graduates maintain high standards, they have the flexibility to make their working life fit with their life outside work.

As well as graduate positions, Ernst & Young offers work experience, summer internship or industrial placement programmes.

EVERSHEDS

Vacancies for around 80 graduates in 2009
For training contracts starting in 2011

 Law

PRIORITISING
PRIORICATOR
COMMUNICATOR

Starting salary for 2009
£35,000

Universities Eversheds plans to visit in 2008-9
Aberdeen, Aston, Bath, Belfast, Birmingham, Bristol, Cambridge, Cardiff, Dublin, Durham, East Anglia, Edinburgh, Exeter, Glasgow, Hull, Kent, Lancaster, Leeds, Leicester, Liverpool, London, Loughborough, Manchester, Northumbria, Nottingham, Nottingham Trent, Oxford, Southampton, St Andrews, Strathclyde, Swansea, Warwick, York
Please check with your university careers service for details of events.

Application deadline
Year-round recruitment
See website for full details.

Contact Details
Turn to page 256 now to request more information or visit our new website at www.top100graduateemployers.com

Eversheds LLP is one of the largest full service international law firms in the world with over 4,000 people and 38 offices in major cities across the UK, Europe and Asia. They work for some of the world's most prestigious organisations in both the public and private sector, offering them a compelling mixture of straightforward advice, clear direction, predictable costs and outstanding service.

It's a winning combination that has meant they are now expanding quicker than any of their closest competitors. Eversheds act for 111 listed companies, including 43 FTSE 250 companies, 30 of the 37 British-based Fortune 500 companies and now have one of the fastest growing corporate teams in the City.

Eversheds has put in place a strategic plan that will see them build on these achievements and grow over the next few years. They are looking for highly ambitious and focused trainees to help them achieve their goals.

Eversheds people are valued for their drive and legal expertise but also for their business advice too. They develop the same qualities in their trainees. Eversheds offer a full, well-rounded training programme with the opportunity to focus technical skills in each of the various practice groups as trainees rotate through four six month seats, while also taking part in a full programme of personal and commercial development skills training too, including finance and business, communication, presenting, business writing, client care, professional standards and advocacy.

WANTED:

RARE TALENTS

The best lawyers are multi-faceted; they combine wit with wisdom and drive with diplomacy. They're competitive but controlled; single-minded yet team oriented.

They're Rare Talents and we're searching for the next generation of them – the Eversheds lawyers and partners of the future. Our training will enhance their existing skills and teach them many new ones. If you've an inkling that you're a Rare Talent – that you're not single-faceted – then satisfy your curiosity at **www.eversheds.com/graduaterecruitment**

 **EVERSHEDS**

ExxonMobil

www.exxonmobil.com/ukrecruitment

**Vacancies for around
55-60 graduates in 2009**

- Accountancy
- Engineering
- Finance
- Human Resources
- IT
- Marketing
- Retailing
- Sales

Starting salary for 2009
£31,500+

**Universities ExxonMobil
plans to visit in 2008-9**
Aberdeen, Aston,
Bath, Belfast,
Birmingham, Cambridge,
Heriot-Watt, Leeds,
London, Loughborough,
Manchester, Newcastle,
Strathclyde, Surrey
Please check with your university
careers service for details of events.

Application deadline
Year-round recruitment

Contact Details
✉ uk.vacancies@exxonmobil.com

Turn to page 256 now to request more
information or visit our new website at
www.top100graduateemployers.com

Exxon Mobil Corporation is the world's largest publicly traded
international oil and gas company, providing energy that helps
underpin growing economies and improve living standards
around the world.

Exxon Mobil Corporation is the parent company of the Esso, Mobil and
ExxonMobil companies that operate in the UK. They operate in a sector that
is dynamic, strategically important and exciting. To secure their position within
this environment the company strives towards operational excellence with
an expert, talented workforce, strong financial resources and cutting-edge
technology. Their customers are both global and local, ranging from major
airlines to the million customers a day who visit their UK service stations.

A broad range of exciting career opportunities are available within both
commercial and technical functions where graduates can expect immediate
responsibility. Graduates progress through specific operational roles, to gain a
broad range of experiences throughout their career with the company. Rapid
skills growth and career development is standard and graduates can expect a
high degree of intellectual challenge and change throughout their career.

The graduate programme, run in conjunction with the internationally renowned
London Business School (LBS), is a two year, modular course covering
business awareness, interpersonal skills and people management. Lecturers
from the LBS deliver the course, aided by ExxonMobil speakers. Graduates
are equipped with a portfolio of skills to help them manage workplace issues,
analyse problems and take appropriate action. Those who successfully
complete the programme are awarded alumni status with the LBS.

By 2030, global energy
demand will increase
by about 30%.

It's a **challenge** like no other.
And it will be solved by someone like **you**.

Aviation
Engineering Specialist
Finance
Geoscience
Human Resources
Information Technology
Sales & Marketing
Production
Refining & Chemicals
One year internships
Summer internships

The need for energy is a very real economic issue. It affects literally everyone – everywhere in the world. At ExxonMobil, we're uniquely positioned to help find the answers to the world's toughest energy challenges. We have the resources, the technology, and the commitment of people just like you.

When you build your career here, you have the opportunity to make a profound impact. From inventing new technologies, to unlocking new sources of petroleum, to developing more efficient fuel and engine systems, you can make the breakthroughs happen.

The biggest challenges attract the best. Whether your background is in business, engineering or science, ExxonMobil has a challenging career waiting for you.

www.exxonmobil.com/ukrecruitment

 **Mobil**

Brands of ExxonMobil

ExxonMobil
Taking on the world's toughest energy challenges.™

FABER MAUNSELL | AECOM

**Vacancies for around
250 graduates in 2009**

Engineering

**Starting salary for 2009
£Competitive**

Faber Maunsell's team of professionals are united by a common purpose – to enhance and sustain the world's built, natural and social environments. Their expertise lies in planning, designing, managing and implementing projects in the buildings, transportation and environmental markets.

**Universities that
Faber Maunsell
plans to visit in 2008-9**

Bath, Belfast, Birmingham,
Bristol, Cambridge, Cardiff,
City, Durham, Edinburgh,
Exeter, Glasgow,
Heriot-Watt, Leeds,
Loughborough, Manchester,
Newcastle, Nottingham,
Oxford, Plymouth,
Sheffield, Southampton,
Strathclyde, Warwick
Please check with your university
careers service for details of events.

As part of AECOM, one of the world's largest global providers of professional technical services, their people get the opportunity to work on truly outstanding projects, such as the Rion Antirion Bridge in Greece (pictured), the Halley VI Antarctic Research Station, and the Strategic Environmental Assessment of Scotland's Marine Renewable Energy Programme.

Faber Maunsell is looking for the brightest and best people to challenge, encourage and support towards acquiring a relevant professional qualification. Applications are encouraged from a wide range of disciplines but particularly those with a degree in a relevant engineering or science-based subject.

Graduate opportunities exist for: civil, structural, mechanical, electrical, transport and environmental engineers; transport and development planners; scientists, ecologists and other specialists.

**Application deadline
Year-round recruitment**

Faber Maunsell operates a comprehensive training academy for all staff, graduate to director, designed to help meet specific and developing training needs.

Graduates benefit from a competitive salary and substantial package of flexible benefits to suit individual needs, including assistance in repaying student loans. Graduates may also be eligible to receive a 'Golden Hello', plus further financial awards for achieving full membership of a relevant professional institution and professional papers published.

Contact Details

✉ graduates@fabermaunsell.com

☎ 020 8784 5784

Turn to page 256 now to request more information or visit our new website at www.top100graduateemployers.com

FABER MAUNSELL | AECOM

At Faber Maunsell, our team of professionals around the world are united by a common purpose – to enhance and sustain the world's built, natural and social environments.

If you are interested in a rewarding career that offers world class projects, global opportunities and award winning training and development programmes you should discover more at www.fabermaunsell.com

Faber Maunsell is an equal opportunities employer.

Foreign & Commonwealth Office

Vacancies for around 30 graduates in 2009

All sectors

Starting salary for 2009
£21,759-£31,290

Universities that The Foreign & Commonwealth Office plans to visit in 2008-9

Bath, Bristol, Cambridge, Durham, Edinburgh, London, Manchester, Nottingham, Oxford
Please check with your university careers service for details of events.

Application deadline
Late November 2008
See website for full details.

Contact Details
✉ faststream@parity.net

Turn to page 256 now to request more information or visit our new website at www.top100graduateemployers.com

The Foreign & Commonwealth Office (FCO) is the lead UK government department handling foreign affairs. This means they deal with child abduction, conflict prevention, forced marriages, blood diamonds, counter terrorism, climate change, counter proliferation, trade and investment, helping British citizens abroad and much more.

They are looking for people who want to be part of a diverse, talented, high performing team working towards a safe, just and prosperous world. They will be forward-thinking, innovative and able to develop new solutions to difficult problems (such as deciding what to do about a missing holiday maker or trying to stop the flow of illegal drugs into the UK).

Successful applicants will spend their first four weeks in a mix of training and exposure to their department. Then they'll work with their manager to determine the training that is best for them – this could range from a two-day course in managing staff to a two-year MBA. Graduates will also have access to a suite of e-learning programmes and be able to take advantage of the coaching and mentoring schemes.

Successful applicants will spend the first two years in London, where one year will be spent doing policy work (such as handling relations with other countries, dealing with security and defence issues or working to improve human rights abroad), then one year will be in a service delivery role (such as working in the consular department helping distressed British nationals). Graduates will then go abroad to work in one of 200 embassies, high commissions or consulates around the world for two to three years.

**Foreign &
Commonwealth
Office**

A GRADUATE CAREER
LIKE NO OTHER

There's no workplace more exciting and diverse than our world – and a graduate career at the Foreign & Commonwealth Office is the perfect way to experience it. We work on everything from climate change to forced marriages to counter terrorism and as you can imagine, the challenge, responsibility and the opportunity to travel is like no other. To find out more visit **www.fco.gov.uk/careers** or apply by selecting Diplomatic Service at **www.faststream.gov.uk**

FRESHFIELDS BRUCKHAUS DERINGER

www.freshfields.com/uktrainees

Vacancies for around 100 graduates in 2009
For training contracts starting in 2011

■ Law

Starting salary for 2009
£39,000

Universities Freshfields Bruckhaus Deringer plans to visit in 2008-9
Belfast, Birmingham, Bristol, Cambridge, City, Durham, Edinburgh, Exeter, Glasgow, Kent, Leeds, Leicester, London, Manchester, Nottingham, Oxford, Sheffield, St Andrews, Warwick, York
Please check with your university careers service for details of events.

Application deadline
31st July 2009

Contact Details
✉ uktrainees@freshfields.com
☎ 020 7427 3194

Turn to page 256 now to request more information or visit our new website at www.top100graduateemployers.com

As a leading international law firm with a network of 27 offices in 16 countries, Freshfields provides first-rate legal services to corporations, financial institutions and governments around the world. With clients such as Morgan Stanley, AstraZeneca, Tesco, EMI and the Bank of England, it is recognised as a market leader for a wide range of work.

Trainee solicitors receive a thorough professional training in a very broad range of practice areas, an excellent personal development programme and the chance to work in one of the firm's international offices or on secondment with a client. Flexibility is one of the hallmarks of their training programme and one of the features which most differentiates the Freshfields training contract from others.

The firm has a friendly and relaxed atmosphere which comes from having a diverse range of individuals who share a strong set of common values. A wide range of social, sporting and cultural activities are available and the firm is known for its pro bono work and CSR programme.

There is no such thing as a 'typical' Freshfields lawyer. The firm's broad array of practice areas and clients demands a wide range of individuals with differing skills, abilities and interests. However, successful candidates will need strong academic qualifications (the ability to achieve a high 2.1 or first at degree level), a broad range of skills and a good record of achievement in other areas.

Vacation placements are offered for students in their penultimate year. See the firm's website for details.

FRESHFIELDS BRUCKHAUS DERINGER

SERIOUSLY HIGH-RISE

FEET ON THE GROUND

Freshfields is one of the world's biggest and most successful law firms. We have over 2,500 lawyers in 27 offices worldwide and are well known for handling large, complex and high-profile cases.

But it isn't the size of our deals or our impressive client list that makes us a special firm – it's our people. We have a friendly and inclusive culture in which making time for each other is important and everyone's contribution is valued. And while we take our work very seriously, we like to take ourselves less so. So if you're high on drive and ambition but down

FUJITSU

Vacancies for around 100+ graduates in 2009

- Consulting
- Finance
- Human Resources
- IT
- Sales

Vacancies also available in Europe.

Starting salary for 2009
£26,000
Plus a £2,000 joining bonus.

Universities that Fujitsu plans to visit in 2008-9
Aston, Bath, Birmingham, Brunel, Cardiff, Leeds, London, Loughborough, Manchester, Reading, Sheffield, Southampton, Warwick
Please check with your university careers service for details of events.

Application deadline
31st January 2009

Contact Details
 fjsgrad2009@alexmann.com
☎ 0870 351 3544

Turn to page 256 now to request more information or visit our new website at www.top100graduateemployers.com

Fujitsu Services business growth over recent years is impressive. They are highly ambitious and their sights are set firmly on continued significant growth over the coming years, both through organic and non-organic means. With an annual turnover of £2.46 billion (€3.59 billion), employing 19,000 people across 20 countries, Fujitsu Services is the European IT services arm of the US$43.2 billion (€32.5 billion) Fujitsu Group – one of the world's largest IT Companies.

Fujitsu cares about career development. That's why they will do their best to help graduates build on their strengths and take the path that's right for them.

When selecting candidates, Fujitsu looks for people, from all degree disciplines, who will bring their own personalities and skills to the role. Graduates who are willing to learn and push themselves. Honest people, who are professional and can communicate well. People with determination, belief and enthusiasm.

Fujitsu's programme involves a comprehensive 18 month modular development programme, designed to cover all the key skills to set graduates up for a career in business. Alongside the training they undertake in their chosen area, there are additional units designed to help successful applicants make sound commercial decisions and develop their business knowledge.

On top of this, as they are looking to attract the best graduates, Fujitsu has a great rewards package designed to help them do just that.

For those who would like to join a company who has built a reputation in the marketplace for realism, straight-talking and tenacity based around a customer-first approach please apply on-line at uk.fujitsu.com/graduates

To be **successful**
you have to be **different**.

You could just **follow** the crowd,
or **stand out** from them.

What do
you want to do?

uk.fujitsu.com/graduates

Vacancies for around
350 graduates in 2009

- Accountancy
- Engineering
- Finance
- IT
- Purchasing
- Research & Development

Starting salary for 2009
£24,000

**Universities that GCHQ
plans to visit in 2008-9**
Please check with your university
careers service for details of events.

Application deadline
Year-round recruitment

Contact Details
✉ recruitment@gchq.gsi.gov.uk

Turn to page 256 now to request more
information or visit our new website at
www.top100graduateemployers.com

GCHQ is one of the UK's three intelligence services, alongside MI5 and MI6. The only one based outside London – in Cheltenham – it has two very specific roles in helping counter threats which compromise national and global security.

The first is to use some of the world's most powerful technology to 'intercept' communications and electronic signals from around the world. Teams of IT, electronics and telecommunications specialists manage the equipment, while mathematicians, linguists and intelligence analysts study and interpret the information it provides. This information is then used by customers – the government, law enforcement agencies and the military – to inform foreign policy or fight terrorism and crime.

The second is to stop hostile forces hacking into and damaging the UK's critical communications infrastructure, including the government's own IT systems. This specialist work is the responsibility of CESG – The National Technical Authority for Information Assurance.

In both, the focus is on keeping one step ahead of people who are, in turn, trying to keep one step ahead of GCHQ. This means the work is constantly evolving, extremely challenging, and always interesting. GCHQ employs around 5,000 people – mainly in Cheltenham – and recruits graduates from all disciplines into entry level roles in a range of operational and support functions.

While the work is totally unique, the skills – and professional qualifications – gained will be industry standard, and transferable. Everyone benefits from personalised training, mentoring and shadowing. Applicants must be British citizens.

it's an interesting world

Conflict in Afghanistan.
Drug smuggling in Europe.
Graduate careers in Cheltenham.

Work for the country. Live in the country. Part of Britain's intelligence services, GCHQ helps counter terrorism and crime – all from our Cheltenham HQ, based in the heart of the Cotswolds. Few careers outside London offer such interesting work, or serious potential. Working here as a graduate is totally unique, and constantly challenging. Once you're through our doors, new pathways will open. And so will your eyes and minds. You'll hear – and see – things you won't find in any other line of work. We're looking for graduates to develop as Language & Culture Specialists, Mathematicians, Intelligence Analysts and IT, Internet and Engineering Specialists. If you're looking for stimulating careers with a meaningful commitment to your work-life balance, find out more at our website.

INVESTOR IN PEOPLE

Applicants must be British citizens. GCHQ values diversity and welcomes applicants from all sections of the community. We want our workforce to reflect the diversity of our work.

www.careersinbritishintelligence.co.uk

GlaxoSmithKline

Vacancies for around 40-50 graduates in 2009

- Engineering
- Finance
- IT
- Logistics
- Manufacturing
- Marketing
- Purchasing
- Research & Development
- Sales

Starting salary for 2009
£Competitive

Universities that GlaxoSmithKline plans to visit in 2008-9
Please check with your university careers service for details of events.

Application deadline
Year-round recruitment

Contact Details
Turn to page 256 now to request more information or visit our new website at www.top100graduateemployers.com

GlaxoSmithKline (GSK) is a place where ideas come to life. As one of the world's leading research-based pharmaceutical companies, GSK is dedicated to delivering products and medicines that help millions of people around the world do more, feel better and live longer.

Based in the UK, but with operations in the US and 117 other countries worldwide, GSK make almost 4 billion packs of medicine and healthcare products every year, with turnover of £22.7 billion in 2007. And much of this is thanks to an extensive product range that includes everything from prescription medicines to popular consumer healthcare products.

So while some people depend on GSK's pioneering pharmaceutical products to tackle life-threatening illnesses, others choose best-selling nutritional brands such as Lucozade and Ribena for a feel-good boost. GSK even manages to brighten smiles with some of the world's favourite toothpaste brands.

New starters at GSK will soon see that there's no such thing as a typical career path at GSK. With roles at all levels, as well as a number of industrial placements, across all business functions, there are plenty of opportunities to learn and develop.

And with so much geographical and business diversity on offer, GSK is in a great position to give all the support needed. There are no limits on where a career could lead – their various development programmes in the UK have produced some of GSK's most inspirational leaders. Find out more about the opportunities on offer by visiting GSK at www.gsk.com/uk-students

SCIENCE

STATISTICS

ENGINEERING

PRODUCTION MANAGEMENT

FINANCE

SALES & MARKETING

IT

REGULATORY AFFAIRS

PURCHASING

YOU'LL BE AMAZED HOW MUCH GOES INTO OUR PRODUCTS.

Graduate Opportunities: Sales, Marketing, Finance, Science, IT, Purchasing, Regulatory Affairs, Statistics, Engineering and Production Management

It's a fact that science is a vital part of what we do. Look beyond that though, and you'll see everything happening at GSK is a real team effort from beginning to end, where a variety of different specialist departments come together to achieve incredible results. And that means as one of the world's leading research-based pharmaceutical and healthcare companies, we're in a great position to offer a wide range of unmissable opportunities to graduates from any degree background.

Discover why our success depends on so much more than science. Visit **www.gsk.com/uk-students**

GSK is proud to promote an open culture, encouraging people to be themselves and giving their ideas a chance to flourish. GSK is an equal opportunity employer.

 GlaxoSmithKline

gsk.com/uk-students

Goldman Sachs

www.gs.com/careers

Vacancies for around
250 graduates in 2009

- Finance
- Human Resources
- Investment Banking
- IT

Vacancies also available in Europe.

Starting salary for 2009
£Competitive

**Universities that
Goldman Sachs
plans to visit in 2008-9**
Please check with your university
careers service for details of events.

Application deadline
19th October 2008

Contact Details
Turn to page 256 now to request more
information or visit our new website at
www.top100graduateemployers.com

Goldman Sachs is a global investment banking, securities and investment management firm. They provide a wide range of services to a substantial and diversified client base that includes corporations, financial institutions, governments, non-profit organisations and high net worth individuals. They bring together people, capital and ideas to make things happen for their clients.

Goldman Sachs' business is structured in a series of specialised divisions: Finance, Global Compliance, Global Investment Research, Legal & Management Controls, Investment Banking; Investment Management; Merchant Banking, Operations, Securities Division and Technology.

Goldman Sachs welcomes graduates from a wide range of university courses and backgrounds. There are a number of different stages when graduates can consider joining Goldman Sachs. Naturally, they will be given different degrees of exposure and responsibility but whether it is as an intern, a new analyst or a new associate, successful applicants will immediately become part of the team with a real and substantial role to play.

Academic discipline is less important than the personal qualities an individual brings with them, however a strong interest in and appreciation of finance is important. Whatever the background, it is intellect, personality and zest for life that the firm values the most.

Goldman Sachs evaluate candidates on six core measures – achievement, leadership, commercial focus, analytical thinking , team work and the ability to make an impact. The firm expects commitment, enthusiasm and drive from its employees but in return, offers unparalleled exposure, early responsibility, significant rewards and unlimited career opportunities.

Goldman Sachs

First job.
Lasting impression.

A chance. An opportunity. A foot in the door. At Goldman Sachs, your first job will give you much more. You'll gain access to unparalleled training programs. Work alongside some of the smartest minds in the financial industry. And gain hands-on experience that will serve you right now, and for years to come.

To find out more about the options available to you and to complete an online application, please visit **gs.com/careers**

Application Deadlines
Fulltime: 19 October 2008
Summer Internships: 07 December 2008
Spring Programme: 01 February 2009

Google

www.google.com/jobs/students

Vacancies for around 40 graduates in 2009

- Engineering
- IT
- Marketing
- Media
- Sales

Vacancies also available in Europe and elsewhere in the world.

Starting salary for 2009
£Competitive

Universities that Google plans to visit in 2008-9
Cambridge, Dublin, Edinburgh, Manchester, Oxford
Please check with your university careers service for details of events.

Application deadline
Year-round recruitment

Contact Details
✉ campuseurope@google.com

Turn to page 256 now to request more information or visit our new website at www.top100graduateemployers.com

Google's mission is to organise the world's information and make it universally accessible and useful. While still committed to building the perfect search engine, their work goes well beyond delivering accurate search results. The spirit of innovation and entrepreneurship that made the company a success right from the start remains strong to this day.

Everyday, Googlers work on new technologies and products which help fulfill this mission. That's why people often compare Google to a start-up – only with resources. They provide employees with the means and the flexible corporate structure they need to forge Google's future, and their own.

Google's strategy is simple: hire great people and support them in turning their aspirations into reality. Googlers are bright, passionate people with diverse backgrounds coming together to create a unique culture. One where the open exchange of ideas is encouraged and thinking beyond the norm expected. Some Googlers love thinking long and hard about difficult problems, others just enjoy spending time with Google users. But all share an enthusiasm for making the world a better place through the intelligent application of information technology.

To continue growing, Google requires ideas from both technical and non-technical fields, and currently has positions available in online advertising, sales, marketing, business development, operations, client support and engineering. New Google employees will get a great introduction to the world of online business, work on innovation products, lead teams, pursue their passions and make a difference both inside the company and in the world.

Get into Google.

Ever considered a career at Google? We're hiring for both technical and non-technical roles!

Apply online NOW including your CV, cover letter and grade summary/transcripts at www.google.com/jobs/students.

Visit www.google.com/jobs/students to learn more about our company and apply.

Google

 **Grant Thornton**

www.graduates.grant-thornton.co.uk

**Vacancies for around
250 graduates in 2009**

Accountancy

Starting salary for 2009
£Competitive

**Universities that
Grant Thornton
plans to visit in 2008-9**

Bath, Belfast, Birmingham,
Bristol, Cambridge, Cardiff,
City, Durham, East Anglia,
Edinburgh, Exeter, Glasgow,
Lancaster, Leeds, Leicester,
Liverpool, London,
Loughborough, Manchester,
Newcastle, Nottingham,
Oxford, Reading, Sheffield,
Southampton, Strathclyde,
Warwick, York
Please check with your university
careers service for details of events.

Application deadline
Year-round recruitment

Contact Details
✉ recruitment@gtuk.com

Turn to page 256 now to request more
information or visit our new website at
www.top100graduateemployers.com

Everyone has big decisions to make. As a leading business and financial adviser with offices in 29 locations nationwide, Grant Thornton UK LLP provides trusted and timely advice to help people make an informed decision.

Led by over 300 partners and employing more than 4,400 of the profession's brightest minds, Grant Thornton provides personalised assurance, tax and specialist advisory services to over 40,000 individuals, privately-held businesses and public interest entities.

Graduates will find themselves working within its assurance, tax, business risk services, recovery and reorganisation or actuarial departments. And they'll benefit from putting their new skills into practice straight away. So whether they're working with a household name or a smaller client, they'll be face-to-face with finance directors, business owners, influential non-executive directors and well-known financial institutions.

Grant Thornton's graduate scheme features training courses held at its dedicated training centre, Bradenham Manor, making the transition to qualified professional as smooth as possible. Beyond qualification, career development will cover specialist and managerial training and the potential to become a partner in the firm.

Trainees work across a variety of different sectors and teams to develop a breadth of skills. There are secondments and transfers available to specialist areas across the firm, and they benefit from an international secondment programme.

Applicants need a minimum of 300 UCAS points (or equivalent) and a 2.1 honours degree, or better, in any discipline. All applicants must have a minimum of B grades in GCSE Mathematics and English language (or equivalent).

Big decisions follow you around.

Where can I be somebody?

Work for a Grant Thornton member firm anywhere in the world and you'll be a valued contributor, right from the start. With a high ratio of partners and directors to staff, you can expect more time with your member firm's leaders and more direct contact with clients. So today's big decision could be tomorrow's reality.

To explore opportunities available at Grant Thornton, visit **www.GrantThorntonDecisions.com**

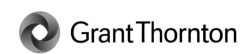

Audit • Tax • Advisory

**Vacancies for around
120 graduates in 2009**

- Accountancy
- Finance
- General Management
- Human Resources
- Investment Banking
- IT
- Marketing
- Retailing
- Sales

Starting salary for 2009
£Competitive

**Universities that HBOS
plans to visit in 2008-9**

Bath, Bristol, Durham,
Edinburgh, Leeds,
London, Manchester,
Nottingham, Sheffield,
St Andrews, Strathclyde
Please check with your university
careers service for details of events.

Application deadline
31st December 2008

Contact Details

Turn to page 256 now to request more
information or visit our new website at
www.top100graduateemployers.com

HBOS is the result of the merger of Halifax and Bank of
Scotland which took place six years ago. Since then, HBOS
has continued to grow into one of the largest companies in
the world with assets of over £590 billion and offices across
17 countries.

With over 72,000 employees worldwide and 22 million customers, HBOS is
also one of the fastest growing banks in the UK. Many may know them as the
umbrella organisation to a wide range of businesses. Some of them, such as
Clerical Medical, Sheila's Wheels and, naturally, Bank of Scotland and Halifax
are household names.

HBOS gives graduates the opportunity to achieve their goals in a wide range
of settings. That's why they are looking for people that are interested in growth
and progression. Whether graduates are interested in Business Leadership,
Commercial Leadership, Finance, Risk, Marketing, HR or a career in one
of their specialist schemes there is a career path that will make the most of
individual talents and ambitions. HBOS believe that encouraging the highest
standards for teamwork will help its employees to find ways to learn and grow.

HBOS are looking for people that are passionate about their work, driven and
ready to take on genuine responsibilities. With plans for continuing progress,
graduates will be able to develop their career by taking advantage of the
endless opportunities.

Most of the graduate schemes require a minimum 2.2 degree or a
2:1 for specialist schemes. For more information please go to
www.hbosbeamazed.co.uk

YOU DON'T NEED TO LEAVE YOUR INDIVIDUALITY AT THE DOOR TO SUCCEED IN FINANCIAL SERVICES.

Graduate Programme 2009

Whether you're capable of remarkable feats in leadership, your fascination for statistics knows no bounds, or your true passion is IT, there's a place for you at HBOS. And that's just the beginning. With a wide variety of businesses stretching across Britain and beyond, we offer choice you won't find anywhere else. If you're a talented graduate looking for variety, we won't disappoint. Ever. Just visit www.hbosbeamazed.co.uk and you'll see what we mean.

**PREPARE to be
amazed**

   Equal opportunities for all - our policy is as simple as that.

www.hbosbeamazed.co.uk

Herbert Smith

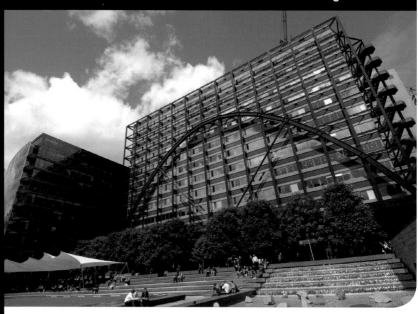

www.herbertsmithgraduates.com

**Vacancies for around
105 graduates in 2009**
For training contracts starting in 2011

 Law

Starting salary for 2009
£37,500

**Universities that
Herbert Smith
plans to visit in 2008-9**
Belfast, Birmingham,
Bristol, Cambridge,
Cardiff, Dublin, Durham,
Edinburgh, Glasgow,
Leeds, Leicester, London,
Manchester, Newcastle,
Nottingham, Oxford,
Reading, Southampton,
Sussex, Warwick
Please check with your university
careers service for details of events.

Application deadline
31st July 2009

Contact Details
✉ graduate.recruitment@
herbertsmith.com
☎ 020 7374 8000

Turn to page 256 now to request more
information or visit our new website at
www.top100graduateemployers.com

Herbert Smith LLP is an international legal practice with 1,200
lawyers across Asia, Europe and the Middle East. In addition,
its Alliance with Gleiss Lutz and Stibbe, as well as a network of
relationship firms across the rest of the world, enables Herbert
Smith to provide a seamless, first class cross-border service.

Herbert Smith's blue-chip client base includes FTSE 100 and Fortune 500
companies, major investment banks and governments. Its strengths span the
width of commercial law and its reputation for innovative legal work crosses
most sectors of industry and commerce. A friendly, collaborative culture prevails
at Herbert Smith and the firm has a powerful worldwide reputation.

Herbert Smith also has a strong reputation for the training it provides. Trainees
will rotate around four seats of six months each. They can also apply for seats
in specialist areas such as IP, tax, trusts, EU/competition, employment, pensions
and incentives or the advocacy unit. Alternatively they can apply to go on
secondment to a client or to one of Herbert Smith's international offices.

The training process at Herbert Smith is carefully balanced between contentious
and non-contentious work; early responsibility and close support. Great
emphasis is placed on professional and personal development, with the firm
running a mentoring scheme as well as its own legal development programme.

As well as a strong academic record, trainees at Herbert Smith thrive on a good
measure of common sense and the presence of mind to find their feet and make
their own way in a large firm.

If applicants can combine these qualities with a creative, questioning mind,
Herbert Smith will offer them an exciting opportunity to develop their careers.

Legal Career *or* Life Investment

Do you want your legal training to turn you into a good lawyer or an exceptional talent?

For more information on our training programme and vacation schemes, and for details on how to apply, please visit our website at:

www.herbertsmithgraduates.com

Herbert Smith

Herbert Smith in association with
Gleiss Lutz and Stibbe

HSBC ◆X◆
The world's local bank

Vacancies for around 300 graduates in 2009

- Finance
- Investment Banking

Vacancies also available in Europe, Asia and the USA.

Starting salary for 2009
£Competitive

Universities that HSBC plans to visit in 2008-9
Birmingham, Bristol, Cambridge, City, London, Loughborough, Manchester, Nottingham, Oxford, Warwick
Please check with your university careers service for details of events.

Application deadline
31st October 2008

Contact Details
Turn to page 256 now to request more information or visit our new website at www.top100graduateemployers.com

With around 330,000 employees and 10,000 offices in 83 countries and territories, HSBC is one of the largest financial services organisations in the world, and one of the few banks with a truly global presence.

HSBC is recognised for combining this truly global reach with local knowledge, the wide range of products and services it offers, and the expertise of its people. HSBC provides a comprehensive range of financial services to over 125 million customers worldwide. The size of the HSBC Group means that it is able to provide a range of financial services to its clients, both national and international. It also means that HSBC can offer its people careers of unlimited potential.

Exceptional graduates of any discipline are recruited onto HSBC's world class training programmes, preparing them for management and executive positions across the business. These include Commercial Management, Executive Management, Insurance Broking, Information Technology, Retail Management, Marketing, HR, European Management, Trainee Financial Planning Management, Operations Management, International Management, Global Banking and Markets, Group Private Banking and Global Asset Management.

HSBC also offers a range of internships to promising undergraduates, both in their first year or penultimate year of study. HSBC is committed to certain key business principles and values. In addition to providing appropriate financial products and following fair, responsible lending policies, HSBC has a strong corporate responsibility programme that contributes to the everyday life of the local communities in which its people work. Employees are encouraged to get involved in HSBC's many educational and environmental projects across the globe.

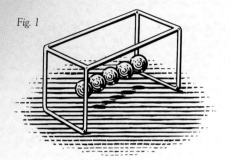

Fig. 1

The Coaster.

*A close relation to the sloth,
this is a lesser-spotted creature
which reacts aggressively
to environmental changes.*

Fig. 2

The Prowler.

*A fierce predator willing to hunt
its prey over any distance,
and has even been known to eat
its young in times of drought.*

Fig. 3

The Follower.

*A domesticated species,
which no longer trusts its instincts.
It is easily panicked
without the security of the herd.*

Fig. 4

The Rare Breed.

*Highly intelligent and versatile,
it integrates well into any environment.
With strong senses it is the most
switched-on of all species.*

HSBC

The world's local bank

If you are a rare breed, please go to **www.hsbc.com/studentcareers**

www.ibm.com/start/uk

Vacancies for around 250 graduates in 2009

- Accountancy
- Consulting
- Finance
- IT
- Logistics
- Research & Development
- Sales

Starting salary for 2009
£25,000+

Universities that IBM plans to visit in 2008-9

Aston, Bath, Belfast, Birmingham, Bristol, Brunel, Cambridge, Cardiff, Durham, Edinburgh, Exeter, Glasgow, Kent, Lancaster, Leeds, Liverpool, London, Loughborough, Manchester, Newcastle, Nottingham, Nottingham Trent, Oxford, Oxford Brookes, Reading, Sheffield, Southampton, St Andrews, Strathclyde, Surrey, Warwick, York
Please check with your university careers service for details of events.

Application deadline
Year-round recruitment

Contact Details
✉ graduate@uk.ibm.com

Turn to page 256 now to request more information or visit our new website at www.top100graduateemployers.com

THE NEXT BIG IDEA FOR AFRICA WILL START@IBM

IBM is the world leader in IT services and consultancy. The staging of a live press conference in a virtual world; enabling gamers to enjoy an enhanced experience; and empowering researchers to collaborate on big issues, such as climate change in Africa, cancer and AIDS. Wherever innovation and technology touch – IBM is likely to be found.

IBM offers clients an end-to-end portfolio of consulting, technology and services combined with the deep business insight to recommend solutions at one end; the delivery and implementation at the other; and all the technology and services along the way. Over the past five years IBM has acquired more than 60 companies to complement and scale our portfolio of products and offerings.

So it follows that IBM can offer graduates more opportunities for growth, attractive benefits and a unique mix of people, business knowledge and technological expertise that helps real companies solve real problems.

With opportunities in Consultancy, IT Services, Software Development, Business, Finance and Sales – IBM are looking for people from any degree background who are expecting a 2:1 in any subject, who are adaptable, driven, good team players and have a passion for the area of work they are applying to.

Graduates begin their IBM career with a new hire induction program which is then complemented by personal, business or technical skills training on an ongoing basis. Wherever your career is heading… there are the tools in place at IBM to enable a graduate's career to be anything he or she wants it to be.

IBM's spirit of innovation, culture of collaboration and inclusion, their values and determination to be 'green' and a good citizen, all make IBM a great place to work.

ADMIT IT.
YOU DON'T KNOW
WHAT IBM DOES.

ibm.com/start/uk

START@IBM

John Lewis Partnership

Vacancies for around 80 graduates in 2009

- Finance
- General Management
- IT
- Retailing

Starting salary for 2009
£24,000+

Universities John Lewis plans to visit in 2008-9
Bath, Birmingham, Durham, Leeds, London, Manchester, Nottingham, Surrey, Warwick
Please check with your university careers service for details of events.

Application deadline
Varies by function
See website for full details.

Contact Details
✉ careers@johnlewis.co.uk

Turn to page 256 now to request more information or visit our new website at www.top100graduateemployers.com

Everyone who works for the John Lewis Partnership (JLP) co-owns the business. That's why, from the moment graduates join, they are Partners, not employees.

The UK's largest department store group, JLP generated record profits in 2007 and a turnover of £6.8 billion. But it's not only a commercial success story. The company also prides itself on its honesty and integrity.

It offers two retail management schemes: one with John Lewis and one with Waitrose; and two Head Office schemes: Finance and Management Services. All feature practical learning, formal courses, short placement and coaching, and give graduates the range of experience they need to reach the highest levels of the business.

The John Lewis retail management scheme helps graduates reach their first Department Manager position within 12-18 months, then progress into senior store management roles or functions like Buying, Merchandising and Distribution. Those who join Waitrose can expect to manage a £multi-million operation as a Department Manager within 12-24 months and run their own store within a few years.

Graduates from any degree discipline can join the Management Services scheme as Trainee Programmers and then specialise in programming, analysis or project management. While JLP's Finance scheme includes support to study for a CIMA/ACCA qualification and develops the skills to drive the growth of a company that aims to double in size over the next decade.

Rewards include one of the best profit-sharing schemes around which in 2007 was equivalent to nine weeks' pay plus discount and other attractive benefits.

Graduate Training Schemes in Retail Management, IT & Finance

Here's something genuinely exclusive: the chance to co-own a £6.8 billion retail giant, have a say in how it's run and enjoy a share of its profits. How do you get your hands on all that? Convince us you're the type of person who can take responsibility for everything from developing business to developing your own career. Whatever your degree discipline, it's drive, initiative and leadership skills that make you Partnership material.

www.jlpjobs.com/graduates   *John Lewis Partnership*

J.P.Morgan

jpmorgan.com/careers

Vacancies for around 300 graduates in 2009

- Finance
- Investment Banking

Vacancies also available in Europe, Asia and the USA.

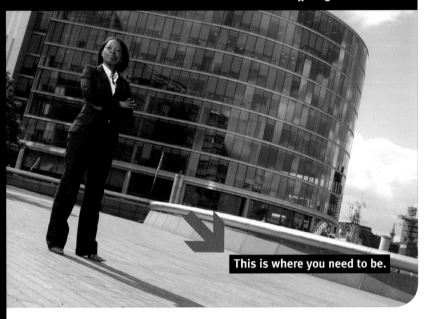

This is where you need to be.

Starting salary for 2009
£Competitive

Universities J.P. Morgan plans to visit in 2008-9
Please check with your university careers service for details of events.

Application deadline
9th November 2008

Contact Details
☎ 020 7325 1000

Turn to page 256 now to request more information or visit our new website at www.top100graduateemployers.com

From the start, J.P. Morgan's goal has been to become the world's most profitable, respected and influential investment bank. Two hundred years on, this hasn't changed. J.P. Morgan is an industry innovator, forcing the pace of change in global finance, executing "first-class business, in a first-class way".

J.P. Morgan is the investment banking business of JPMorgan Chase, a leading global financial services firm with assets of more than $1.6 trillion and operations in over 50 countries. J.P. Morgan serve the interests of clients who have complex financial needs, whether they are major corporations, governments, private firms, financial institutions, non-profit organisations or private individuals.

The global training programmes combine on-the-job learning with classroom instruction that is on a par with the world's finest business schools. Graduates will gain exposure to different parts of the business, giving a multi-dimensional perspective of the company. As a result, they'll emerge not only with a thorough grounding in a particular business area, but a broad experience of the wider commercial picture and a range of transferable business skills, from project management to team leadership.

J.P. Morgan are looking for team-players and future leaders with exceptional drive, creativity and interpersonal skills. Impeccable academic credentials are important, but so are achievements outside the classroom. Graduate opportunities and internships are available across all areas – Investment Banking, Sales, Trading & Research, Asset Management, Risk, Technology, Finance, Operations & Business Services.

OUR STRENGTH IS YOUR OPPORTUNITY.

At J.P. Morgan, we boast the world's finest minds. We work as a team. We win as a team. And inclusivity is everything. That difference is our strength. Make it yours. Join our award winning internship and graduate programmes. **This is where you need to be.**

jpmorgan.com/careers

**Vacancies for around
1,000 graduates in 2009**

	Accountancy
	Finance
	Human Resources
	IT
	Marketing
	Sales

Vacancies also available in Europe.

Starting salary for 2009
£Competitive

**Universities that KPMG
plans to visit in 2008-9**
Aberdeen, Aston, Bath,
Birmingham, Bristol,
Cambridge, Cardiff,
City, Dundee, Durham,
East Anglia, Essex, Exeter,
Edinburgh, Glasgow, Heriot-
Watt, Kent, Lancaster,
Leeds, Leicester, London,
Loughborough, Manchester,
Newcastle, Nottingham,
Oxford, Plymouth, Reading,
Sheffield, Southampton,
St Andrews, Strathclyde,
Surrey, Sussex, Swansea,
Warwick, York
Please check with your university
careers service for details of events.

Application deadline
Year-round recruitment

Contact Details
✉ ukfmgraduate@kpmg.co.uk
☎ 0500 664 665

Turn to page 256 now to request more
information or visit our new website at
www.top100graduateemployers.com

KPMG is part of an international network of business advisers
with almost 100,000 people across their global network in nearly
150 countries. In the UK, they have over 10,000 partners and
staff and provide clients with audit, tax and advisory services
from more than 20 offices.

KPMG in the UK is also one of the leading employers of graduates, and offers a
wide range of high-quality, challenging careers to people from every academic
discipline. There are over 20 different graduate career routes to choose from
within KPMG, each of which offers a great balance of structured support and
real business challenge. Many of their graduate careers also lead to highly
respected and globally-recognised professional qualifications.

The opportunity to gain qualifications doesn't stop when graduates pass the
requisite exams for their area. Depending on the career path, they may wish
to develop language skills, study for an Executive MBA or even embark on a
secondment within an overseas KPMG member firm or in another organisation.

KPMG has recently been named 'Best Big Company to Work For' in The
Sunday Times Best Companies awards 2008 and voted 'Employer of the Year'
by Accountancy Age. The CBI also named the firm 'Big Four Auditor of the
Year' (jointly with Ernst & Young) for the fourth year running.

This is an exciting and dynamic time to join KPMG. The merger of the UK
firm with member firms in Europe to create KPMG Europe LLP will make it
the largest fully integrated accountancy firm in Europe – capable not only of
meeting the needs of the firm's increasingly global clients, but also giving a
range of international challenges and opportunities to the firm's talented people.

The Sunday Times Best Big Company to Work For 2008

No.1

KPMG has consistently been voted in the top three of The Sunday Times 'Best Big Companies to Work For' for four years running.

AUDIT ▪ TAX ▪ ADVISORY

WORLD LEADER IN BEAUTY PRODUCTS

www.lorealbusinessclass.co.uk

Vacancies for around 30 graduates in 2009

- Engineering
- Finance
- Logistics
- Marketing
- Sales

Starting salary for 2009
£27,500+

Universities that L'Oréal plans to visit in 2008-9
Bath, Cambridge, Dublin, London, Manchester, Nottingham, Oxford
Please check with your university careers service for details of events.

Application deadline
Final: 30th June 2009
See website for full details.

Contact Details
Turn to page 256 now to request more information or visit our new website at www.top100graduateemployers.com

With more than 130 products sold per second worldwide, L'Oréal is the global leader in cosmetics. L'Oréal's brand portfolio includes some of the world's most recognised beauty and fragrance brands: L'Oréal Paris, Lancôme, Kérastase, Ralph Lauren, Garnier, Biotherm, Maybelline and Body Shop.

With 63,358 people employed in over 58 countries and 25 global brands sold in more than 130 nations, L'Oréal is a committed Investor in People.

The company is looking to recruit entrepreneurs with a creative flair who want to be challenged and are willing to take on responsibilities from day one.

Each year L'Oréal offers 30 graduate Management Trainees the opportunity to join a year-long, individually tailored programme providing three on-the job placements in different business areas. At L'Oréal graduates work across diverse functions: marketing, sales, PR, market research, visual merchandising, logistics or HR in order to get a 360° exposure to the company's business.

At L'Oréal graduates are encouraged to excel and are guided at every step. They receive expert training on topics related to professional development, business knowledge and personal impact. At L'Oréal, graduates are nurtured to become future General Managers of the company and lead a career of international scope.

The company's stimulating, motivating, open-minded and dynamic culture is a key factor in making L'Oréal the No. 1 FMCG employer of choice.

Learning for development, dedicated mentors, flexible working environment and the company's energetic culture lead to graduates pursuing international fast-track careers.

Linklaters

Vacancies for around
130 **graduates in 2009**
For training contracts starting in
September 2011 and March 2012

Law

Starting salary for 2009
£37,400

**Universities Linklaters
plans to visit in 2008-9**
Belfast, Birmingham,
Bristol, Cambridge,
Dublin, Durham, Edinburgh,
Exeter, Glasgow, Leeds,
Leicester, London,
Manchester, Northumbria,
Nottingham, Oxford,
Sheffield, Southampton,
St Andrews, Warwick
Please check with your university
careers service for details of events.

Application deadline
See website for full details.

Contact Details
✉ graduate.recruitment@
linklaters.com
Turn to page 256 now to request more
information or visit our new website at
www.top100graduateemployers.com

Linklaters is a global law firm that advises the world's leading companies, financial institutions and governments on their most important and challenging transactions and assignments. This is an ambitious and innovative firm which aims to become the leading premium global law firm. Its drive to create something new in professional services provides a very special offer to graduates.

While many law firms have strengths in particular areas, Linklaters is strong across the full range of commercial, corporate and financial law. This makes the firm a particularly stimulating place to train as a business lawyer.

The firm recruits graduates from both law and non-law disciplines. Non-law graduates spend a conversion year at law school taking the Graduate Diploma in Law (GDL). All trainees have to complete the Legal Practice Course (LPC) before starting their training contracts. The firm meets the costs of both the GDL and LPC and provides a maintenance grant for both. The training contract is built around four six-month seats or placements in a range of practice areas. The majority of their trainees have the opportunity to go on international and/or client secondments.

Linklaters people come from many different backgrounds and cultures; by working together to achieve great things for clients, they are encouraged to achieve their own ambitions and potential. With global opportunities, entrepreneurial freedom and world-class training, Linklaters trainees work alongside some of the world's best lawyers on some of the world's most challenging deals. The firm has high expectations of its trainees, but the rewards – personal and professional as well as financial – are very high indeed.

Where will a global career take you?

This is about ambition – ours as well as yours. We aim to become the leading premium global law firm. And we're looking for people who can make it happen. This is why we have so much to offer graduates who want to build a professional career on a world stage. The majority of our trainees spend time in our international offices before qualifying; all of them work on complex, multi-jurisdictional deals and projects. Discover how far you might go with Linklaters. **www.linklaters.com/ukgrads**

Lloyds TSB | for the journey...

www.lloydstsbjobs.co.uk/talent

Vacancies for around 150 graduates in 2009

- Finance
- General Management
- Human Resources
- Investment Banking
- IT
- Retailing

Starting salary for 2009
£25,000/£30,000

Salary dependent on programme.
Plus £5,000 sign on bonus.

Universities Lloyds TSB plans to visit in 2008-9

Aston, Bath, Belfast, Birmingham, Bristol, Cambridge, Durham, Edinburgh, Lancaster, Leicester, London, Nottingham, Oxford, Southampton, St Andrews, Surrey, Warwick

Please check with your university careers service for details of events.

Application deadline
31st January 2009

Contact Details

Turn to page 256 now to request more information or visit our new website at www.top100graduateemployers.com

With almost 80,000 employees and a presence in 20 countries, Lloyds TSB is one of the UK's largest and most successful financial services organisations. Their business portfolio includes pensions, investments, corporate markets and insurance, as well as respected brands including Scottish Widows and Cheltenham & Gloucester. This year marks the launch of a totally revised Graduate Leadership Programme, designed to build the Lloyds TSB leaders of tomorrow.

Working closely with each individual to ensure their development needs are met, the two year programme focuses on technical expertise, and on enabling graduates to practise their leadership and management skills on carefully selected assignments. There are a choice of programmes – including general management, finance, corporate markets, HR, retail leadership and IT.

Reflecting the importance – and potential – of these placements, there are a relatively small number of openings, each carrying a high degree of expectation. Everyone will have access to a Senior Manager and a dedicated Graduate Development Specialist, and all will enjoy their own totally unique career journey. This will include formal training, one-on-one reviews and placements to build up management skills and leadership qualities. Where applicable, study towards professional qualifications will form part of the mix.

Successful applicants will need a minimum 2:1, in any discipline, together with all the qualities that make for strong leaders: judgement, drive, the ability to influence and successfully put plans and ideas into action.

As well as exceptional development opportunities, graduates can expect first-class rewards and benefits.

Recognition takes you further, faster.

So hold on tight.

Graduate Leadership Programme

General Management / Finance / HR / Corporate Markets / IT / Retail Leaders

With a small and select graduate intake, your achievements will be recognised. That's why our Leadership Programme has been designed to ensure you thrive in the spotlight. Over the 2 year programme, you'll develop your judgement, influencing skills and ability to deliver on carefully selected assignments. Make no mistake. This is a challenging programme that will thoroughly test your drive and motivations. But with these same qualities – and a good degree – we'll make sure you reach your full potential within one of the UK's largest and most successful financial services organisations. Find out more on our website.

lloydstsbjobs.co.uk/talent

official partner

Lloyds TSB | for the journey...

Lovells

Vacancies for around 90+ graduates in 2009
For training contracts starting in 2011

■ Law

Starting salary for 2009
£37,000

Universities that Lovells plans to visit in 2008-9
Belfast, Birmingham, Bristol, Cambridge, Cardiff, City, Dublin, Durham, Exeter, Leeds, London, Manchester, Newcastle, Nottingham, Oxford, Sheffield, Southampton, St Andrews, Warwick, York
Please check with your university careers service for details of events.

Application deadline
31st July 2009

Contact Details
✉ recruit@lovells.com

Turn to page 256 now to request more information or visit our new website at www.top100graduateemployers.com

Lovells is an international legal practice comprising Lovells LLP and its affiliated businesses. The firm has offices in the major financial and commercial centres across Europe, Asia, the Middle East and the USA.

Lovells' international strength across a wide range of practice areas gives them an exceptional reputation not only for corporate transactional work, but also for other specialist areas including dispute resolution, banking, intellectual property, and employment, EU/competition, insurance and commercial.

The firm recruits high calibre graduates who demonstrate strong intellectual ability, ambition, sound commercial awareness and a good mix of commercial and interpersonal skills.

A trainee at Lovells spends six months in four different areas of practice to gain as broad a range of experience as possible, including the option to spend time with a client or one of the firm's international offices. This experience is underpinned by a comprehensive training programme that includes the Professional Skills Course. Training and experience is tailored to the trainees' individual development and regular appraisals and reviews take place throughout the training contract.

Lovells offer up to 90 vacation placements on four extremely popular schemes held at Christmas, Easter and during the summer. Places are open to penultimate-year law, final year law students, recent graduates and those considering a change of career. The opporuntity also exists to spend time in one of their international offices as part of the Vacation Scheme.

WE'RE WIDE AWAKE
24 HOURS A DAY

How wide is your world?

To find out more about training at Lovells visit our graduate website:

www.lovells.com/graduates

YOUR M&S

www.marksandspencer.com/gradcareeers

**Vacancies for around
100 graduates in 2009**

- Human Resources
- IT
- Purchasing
- Retailing

Starting salary for 2009
£24,000-£25,500

**Universities that
Marks & Spencer
plans to visit in 2008-9**
Please check with your university
careers service for details of events.

Application deadline
December 2008

Contact Details
Turn to page 256 now to request more
information or visit our new website at
www.top100graduateemployers.com

When it comes to offering graduates a thorough grounding in retail, the Marks & Spencer scheme is hard to beat.

The scheme involves taking on three or four placements over the course of around 12 months. Alongside this on-the-job training, graduates receive classroom tuition, designed to help them develop expert knowledge, as well as personal skills in areas such as negotiation and leadership. By the end of the scheme, they should have everything they need to take on their first big management role. That could mean leading a team of people or running an area of the business worth millions of pounds. In all likelihood, it will mean both.

Most M&S graduates join them in a store-based role, and are placed on a fast-track route into senior level retail management. If everything goes as planned, then this will mean running a small store – or a whole department of a large one – after about a year.

Alternatively, they can join an 18-month store-based HR programme. This route offers the chance to develop specialist skills and expertise, gain professional qualifications, and build a successful, long-term HR career.

There are also places available in a range of head office areas, including IT, buying and merchandising, garment and food technology, as well as opportunities for undergraduates to do 12-month business placements.

M&S aren't just looking for any graduates. They're looking for the best around. People with the drive and ambition to make the most of all the opportunities on offer. And people who can match the energy, vision and ideas that have kept M&S at the forefront of their industry for so long.

This is not just any graduate scheme.

www.marksandspencer.com/gradcareers

MARS
incorporated

www.mars.com/ultimategrads

Vacancies for around 30+ graduates in 2009

- Engineering
- Finance
- General Management
- Marketing
- Purchasing
- Research & Development
- Sales

Starting salary for 2009
£29,000+

Universities that Mars plans to visit in 2008-9
Bath, Bristol, Cambridge, Edinburgh, Leeds, Manchester, Nottingham, Oxford, Warwick
Please check with your university careers service for details of events.

Application deadline
10th November 2008
See website for full details.

Contact Details
Turn to page 256 now to request more information or visit our new website at www.top100graduateemployers.com

Discover a world where the only string attached to freedom is responsibility.

Mars®, Uncle Ben's®, Snickers®, Whiskas®, M&M's®, Dolmio®, Twix®, Pedigree®, Maltesers®... these are just some of the household name brands that form the global, $25bn Mars portfolio, making it one of the world's biggest consumer goods companies.

But it's the unique culture that separates Mars from the rest. Based on their five principles, over 48,000 associates in more than 66 countries enjoy the degree of freedom and responsibility unparalleled in the business world.

Still a family-run business and entirely privately owned, Mars is able to invest their own profits in developing the organisation. This means associates have the freedom to think differently and do things normal convention wouldn't allow. With this being the case, Mars graduates get all the support, freedom and responsibility they need. But ultimately, it's the graduates themselves that drive their projects forward, and shape things as they go along.

Whether their talents lie in research and development, engineering, sales, marketing, finance, procurement or general management, Mars' renowned development programmes offer responsibility right from the very first day. Graduates get to work on real projects, carefully chosen to suit their development needs. Support in the pursuit of professional qualifications with financial sponsorship, study leave and regular two-way feedback is a given.

Structured around a rigorous training curriculum and strong individual mentoring relationships, the programmes offer talented individuals an opportunity to take their career in their own hands while benefiting from the years of experience in developing some of the UK's leading managers.

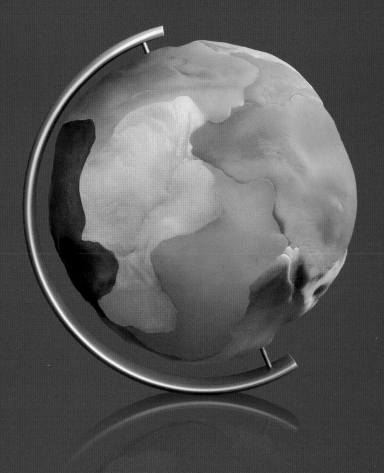

Discover a world which
people are constantly shaping.

We're still the same family-owned business that started out back in 1911, only now
we're quite a bit bigger. With an annual turnover of $25 billion, 48,000 employees, and
a presence in 66 countries, we're able to offer our graduates the strength, stability and
freedom to grow with fewer restrictions. Mars' renowned development programmes
offer real responsibility right from the very first day. Together, we'll shape our own destiny.

Freedom takes courage. We take the courageous.      mars.com/ultimategrads

® Registered Trademark

i'm lovin' it

www.mcdonalds.co.uk/careers

Vacancies for around
150 graduates in 2009

■ General Management
■ Retailing

Starting salary for 2009
£18,500-£21,500
Depending on location.

Universities McDonald's
plans to visit in 2008-9
Please check with your university
careers service for details of events.

Application deadline
Year-round recruitment

Contact Details
✉ mcdcareers@uk.mcd.com
☎ 020 8700 7007
Turn to page 256 now to request more
information or visit our new website at
www.top100graduateemployers.com

Forget the myth that says McDonald's only offers McJobs.
The reality is very different – and far more interesting.
McDonald's management careers offer exceptional challenge
and support, some excellent rewards and all the potential of a
world-famous brand.

Their 20-week management development programme prepares graduates
for running a restaurant – Business Management as they call it. This is
commercial management in its fullest sense. Graduates gain valuable
operational experience in the restaurants, and, as importantly, benefit from
wide-ranging commercial exposure. They cover everything from leadership
and people development to cash control and profit maximisation.

Provided they excel on the programme, within a few years of joining graduates
could be managing a £million business with a 60-strong team: a McDonald's
restaurant. After that they join a management career path that could lead to
Executive team level. Naturally, not everyone will climb that high. But as long
as they have leadership potential and can make the most of the award-winning
training, there's no reason why graduates shouldn't set their sights high.

McDonald's urges graduates to do some soul-searching before applying.
McDonald's managers set the tone of their restaurants, bringing the best
out of their team. To build their businesses, they have to display energy,
commitment and hard work every day. And they need to combine both
decisiveness and sensitivity; ideas and action. Only by blending all these
qualities will graduates excel on one of the most stimulating management
development programmes around.

I love that I can go right to the top.

PAUL, ESSEX

MY MᶜJOB

With management training that reflects the latest thinking and
wins awards, your career can go as far as you want it to.

Apply at mcdonalds.co.uk/careers

McKinsey&Company

www.mckinsey.com/careers

Vacancies for no fixed quota of **graduates in 2009**

■ **Consulting**

Vacancies also available in Europe, Asia, the USA and elsewhere in the world.

Starting salary for 2009
£Competitive

Universities that McKinsey & Company plans to visit in 2008-9
Bath, Bristol, Cambridge, Dublin, Edinburgh, London, Oxford, St Andrews
Please check with your university careers service for details of events.

Application deadline
Year-round recruitment

Contact Details
✉ london_opportunities@mckinsey.com
☎ 020 7961 7070

Turn to page 256 now to request more information or visit our new website at www.top100graduateemployers.com

McKinsey & Company is a place where recent graduates can have immediate and direct contact with some of the world's top CEOs and public leaders and where their opinions are encouraged and valued.

As a leading global management consultancy, McKinsey's goal is to provide distinctive and long-lasting performance improvements to clients, which range from governments and multinationals to charities and entrepreneurial firms.

As business analysts, graduates work as part of a small team comprising of McKinsey colleagues from around the world, as well as client representatives. Dedicated to one project at a time, they contribute fully: gathering and analysing data; interviewing, coaching and listening; making recommendations; and presenting the team's findings to the client. McKinsey's work cuts across every business sector; from multimedia to energy, banking to retail, and e-commerce to healthcare.

McKinsey provides invaluable skills, hands-on experience and a thorough grounding in the commercial world. Business analysts are supported with day-to-day mentoring and coaching, coupled with comprehensive training programmes from day one, which equip consultants to become leaders within McKinsey or beyond. McKinsey's commitment to development begins prior to joining with funding for overseas language tuition and training in business basics.

McKinsey believes that bright, highly motivated newcomers to the business world can bring fresh and innovative insights to the organisation's consideration of the challenges facing our clients. Each year, McKinsey hires a number of outstanding graduates and masters degree students from a diverse range of academic disciplines as business analysts.

greater
expectations

We welcome applications from all degree
disciplines. To find out more please visit
www.mckinsey.com

McKinsey&Company

Merrill Lynch

ml.com/careers/europe

Vacancies for around 300 graduates in 2009

- Finance
- Human Resources
- Investment Banking
- IT
- Research & Development

Vacancies also available in Europe.

Starting salary for 2009
£Competitive

Universities Merrill Lynch plans to visit in 2008-9
Bristol, Cambridge, Durham, London, Oxford, Warwick
Please check with your university careers service for details of events.

Application deadline
31st October 2008

Contact Details
Turn to page 256 now to request more information or visit our new website at www.top100graduateemployers.com

Merrill Lynch is a leading wealth management, capital markets and advisory company with offices on six continents. Full-time and internship programmes are offered in the following areas: Global Markets, Global Investment Banking, Global Wealth Management, Research, Technology and Human Resources.

Upon joining one of Merrill Lynch's full-time programmes, graduates start with an intensive induction. This introduction allows the opportunity to meet, work and socialise with other new analysts from around the world.

On return to the local office, successful applicants will get to grips with professional projects, whilst Merrill Lynch will provide them with a grounding in all of the tools, techniques and work practices that will be required to succeed.

Penultimate year students will have the opportunity to gain an insight into Merrill Lynch through their nine-week summer programme. This is an opportunity to meet management, analysts and other interns through a range of networking activities.

Prior to the penultimate year, students can also compete with a team of colleagues by taking the Merrill Lynch Challenge. The finalist teams participate in a one-week programme in London.

Ambitious, confident and highly motivated, successful applicants will be natural team players with a desire for a future in financial services. Whatever the academic background, graduates must have an inquiring mind with the ability to communicate complex messages in a clear, simple way. Relevant work experience and foreign languages are also an advantage.

global reputation

[limitless potential]

growth and success

inspiring colleagues

Merrill Lynch is one of the world's leading wealth management, capital markets and advisory companies. Our iconic brand and global capabilities offer you the chance to realise your potential whilst working side-by-side with thought leaders on projects of breathtaking scope and complexity. Join us and you can also benefit from a performance-based culture of excellence, where respect for the individual, commitment to breakthrough, big-picture thinking and enduring values create an environment for your continued growth and success.

We must receive your completed application by **Friday 31st October 2008** for the Full-Time programme and **Monday 15th December 2008** for the Summer Internship programme.

For more information or to apply online, please visit **ml.com/careers/europe**

ml.com/careers/europe

Merrill Lynch is an equal opportunity employer.

| Global Markets & Investment Banking | Global Research | Global Wealth Management

Merrill Lynch

 **Met Office**

**Vacancies for around
100 graduates in 2009**

- Consulting
- Engineering
- Finance
- General Management
- Human Resources
- IT
- Marketing
- Purchasing
- Research & Development
- Sales

Starting salary for 2009
£21,000

**Universities the Met Office
plans to visit in 2008-9**
Please check with your university
careers service for details of events.

Application deadline
Year-round recruitment

Contact Details
✉ HRenquiries@metoffice.gov.uk

Turn to page 256 now to request more
information or visit our new website at
www.top100graduateemployers.com

A world-leading expert in weather forecasting and climate change research, the Met Office supports many people and organisations – from the general public, government and local authorities, to aviation, utilities, transport and almost every other industry sector.

With a world-class scientific reputation, the Met Office monitors and analyses climate change, giving expert advice to governments, businesses, and societies. Met Office consultants work with businesses to assess climate change impacts and develop plans for mitigation and adaptation.

Being able to predict the weather for the next hour, day, five days or ten, and seasonal and longer-term climate forecasts, makes the Met Office crucial to commercial business and Government policy decision-making and planning. Although high performance supercomputers are essential for Numerical Weather Prediction and climate change research, it is the combined talents and commitment of the people that really drives the Met Office.

While the core business of the Met Office is centred on forecasting and scientific research, there are also opportunities across a broad spectrum of business disciplines, including Information Technology, Engineering, Sales & Marketing, Consulting and Corporate Services (such as HR, Finance, Legal and Procurement). Some roles are available in locations all over the UK and abroad, but most are based and at the state-of-the-art headquarters in Exeter which has a fitness suite, restaurant and coffee shop, making it an enviable and inspiring environment in which to build a successful career.

Met Office

Brighter

Make a difference
by working for the Met Office

METROPOLITAN POLICE

Working together for a safer London

Vacancies for around TBC graduates in 2009

- Accountancy
- Finance
- General Management
- Human Resources
- IT
- Marketing
- Media
- Research & Development

Starting salary for 2009
£30,432
On completion of initial
31 weeks' training.

Universities that the Met plans to visit in 2008-9
Please check with your university careers service for details of events.

Application deadline
Year-round recruitment

Contact Details
Turn to page 256 now to request more information or visit our new website at www.top100graduateemployers.com

The Metropolitan Police Service is continually evolving and improving to respond to the needs of millions of people of all nationalities, faiths and cultures who visit, live and work in London. The organisation aims to deliver quality policing that reduces crime – and the fear of crime – across the capital. It is also recognised on a global scale as a leading authority on policing today.

The Met today is a far cry from the organisation that was founded in 1829 by Home Secretary Sir Robert Peel. Back then, there were just 1,000 officers looking after a population of 2 million. Now, there are some 50,000 officers and staff working as one team to make the streets safer for 7.2 million Londoners in 32 boroughs across 620 square miles.

As the capital's largest employer, the Met is committed to having a workforce that reflects the community it serves. People join from all kinds of backgrounds, bringing all sorts of skills and experience to a huge diversity of roles. As well as frontline officers, the Met employs 14,000 police staff who carry out vital work such as answering emergency calls, forensics, handling finances or harnessing the latest advancements in technology.

But London can only be policed with the trust and respect of all Londoners, so it's essential that everyone who joins has the sensitivity to work effectively with the many different communities that make up the capital.

Making London safer is uniquely challenging but uniquely rewarding. Good salaries are supplemented by attractive benefits including a superb pension and opportunities for career progression.

WILL YOUR DEGREE MAKE THINGS ANY BETTER?

You can't use your degree certificate as a tissue to wipe away the tears. Neither can you use it as a sticking plaster to patch up the past. But it can still make seven million Londoners feel safe.

We won't treat you any differently just because you're a graduate. Instead, we'll take what you've learnt, move it out of the examination hall and apply it to the real world. Then it's up to you.

Discover what your qualifications really qualify you for. Seven million Londoners are depending on it.

Find out how much by going to
www.metpolicecareers.co.uk

We particularly welcome applications from students from under-represented communities.

METROPOLITAN POLICE   Working together for a safer London   me+ GRADUATES

SECURITYSERVICE
MI5

www.mi5careers.gov.uk

Vacancies for around TBC graduates in 2009

- Engineering
- Finance
- Human Resources
- IT

Starting salary for 2009
£Varies by function
See website for full details.

Universities that MI5 plans to visit in 2008-9
Please check with your university careers service for details of events.

Application deadline
Year-round recruitment

Contact Details
Turn to page 256 now to request more information or visit our new website at www.top100graduateemployers.com

MI5 is the UK's security intelligence agency. Through the collection, dissemination and analysis of intelligence MI5 protects the nation's people, economy and institutions from threats such as terrorism and espionage. To do this takes talented people from a range of backgrounds.

MI5 offers a range of careers. So whatever degree graduates might have it is likely there is a role that suits their skills and abilities. MI5 also looks for a strong range of personal qualities.

Many graduates join as intelligence officers. This demanding and rewarding role involves assessing or investigating threats to national security. Most intelligence officers move departments every 18 months to three years so as well as investigative work a career could include policy, personnel, finance or operational work. Intelligence officers have their own areas of responsibility but work as part of a team.

There are also career opportunities as administrative assistants and business support officers, data analysts, mobile surveillance officers, working in their language unit and a range of IT roles.

As well as vital and varied work, there are lots of other benefits. Training and development programmes give a broader understanding of the organisation and equip staff with the specialist skills needed to make the most of the career opportunities available. The salary and rewards are competitive and include a generous pension scheme and holiday entitlement. Graduates joining the organisation can look forward to working with people from a range of backgrounds in a friendly, team-orientated working environment with a strong sense of shared purpose.

SECURITY SERVICE
MI5

Intelligence. We rely on yours.

mi5careers.gov.uk/intelligence

TOURIST?

As an **Intelligence Officer**, you'll help decide. You'll be faced with some of the most challenging issues facing national security today. And the decisions you make will play a major part in helping to overcome them. Salaries start at £23,500 with excellent benefits. Visit our website to find out more.

ADMINISTRATIVE ASSISTANTS DATA ANALYSTS **ENGLISH LANGUAGE TRANSCRIBERS** INTELLIGENCE OFFICERS **IT CAREERS** PROCUREMENT ROLES **LANGUAGE UNIT** MOBILE SURVEILLANCE OFFICERS **COMPUTER & NETWORK SPECIALISTS**

Microsoft®

Your potential. Our passion.™

www.microsoft.com/uk/graduates

Vacancies for around 30 graduates in 2009

- ■ IT
- ■ Marketing
- ■ Sales

Starting salary for 2009
£26,000
Plus a sign-on bonus.

Universities Microsoft plans to visit in 2008-9
Aston, Bath, Birmingham, Brunel, Kent, Leeds, Loughborough, Manchester, Reading, Warwick
Please check with your university careers service for details of events.

Application deadline
January 2009

Contact Details
✉ gradrec@microsoft.com

Turn to page 256 now to request more information or visit our new website at www.top100graduateemployers.com

Microsoft have created an environment where people can do their best. Hard work is expected, but graduates and students are free to satisfy their intellectual curiosity. Microsoft is somewhere people can think along new lines, explore truly exciting technologies and actually enjoy spending time.

The people who flourish at Microsoft are natural communicators with inquisitive natures, a passion for technology and an instinctive understanding of customers. But what really sets them apart is a drive that raises them above the average whether they join commercial or technical business groups.

The 'Microsoft Academy for University Hires' (MACH) provides the perfect transition between academic and professional life. Although challenging, it equips graduates with the professional skills and know-how required for a rewarding and successful career at Microsoft. Graduates will genuinely tackle unchartered territory, whether working in a technical, sales or marketing role. It might mean discovering how others work or thinking along new lines. Either way, successful applicants will be stepping outside their comfort zone.

The graduate programme includes residential courses at international locations and self-directed learning. Graduates will be given real responsibility, whilst also having the support of managers and mentors throughout. The basic requirements are a 2:1, creativity, vision, people skills, an inquiring mind and a willingness to learn.

The emphasis during student placements in Reading or London is on supplementing theory learnt at university with real, practical experience. The 48-week scheme starts in July with a week-long induction. Training can include residential courses and self-directed learning.

Whatever you do at Microsoft, express yourself.

The Microsoft Academy for University Hires (MACH) is a two year programme designed to take passionate graduates and set them on one of many diverse careers paths across our technical, sales and marketing groups.

Over the course of the programme, we'll provide you with the theoretical and practical skills you need to complement your academic achievements. We'll also ensure that you have the business acumen to make a real difference at the highest levels. By the time you graduate from MACH, you'll have the language to express yourself compellingly, the tools to take on any challenge and the ability to deliver solutions with the power to touch the lives of people all over the world.

Graduate to a more expressive future:

www.microsoft.com/uk/graduates

**DEFENCE ENGINEERING
AND SCIENCE GROUP**

MINISTRY OF DEFENCE

www.desg.mod.uk

**Vacancies for around
110 graduates in 2009**

 Engineering

IT

Starting salary for 2009
£Competitive

**Universities that the MOD
plans to visit in 2008-9**
Please check with your university
careers service for details of events.

Application deadline
See website for full details.

Contact Details
✉ sit-desgmktman@mod.uk
☎ 01225 449368

Turn to page 256 now to request more
information or visit our new website at
www.top100graduateemployers.com

The Defence Engineering and Science Group (DESG) is the
team of thousands of engineers and scientists working within
the Ministry of Defence.

The UK needs modern battle winning forces to defend its interests and to
contribute to strengthening international peace and security. Cutting edge
engineering and science is a critical component in supporting this effort.
The MOD is proud to offer graduates the opportunity to join what is
probably the very best graduate development scheme for engineers and
scientists in the UK: The Ministry of Defence, Defence Engineering and Science
Graduate Scheme.

This prestigious graduate scheme is accredited by: IET, IMechE, RINA, IoP,
RAeS and ICE and has been an industry leader for almost thirty years, launching
hundreds of graduates into satisfying careers in engineering and science. It is
because of the requirement to safeguard the UK and its interests that the DESG
can offer a huge range and depth of development opportunities – making it a
market leader.

Moreover, it is the quality of the training programme, the accelerated path to
chartership, personal mentoring and huge investment in each graduate that
sets this apart from competitors in the engineering and science field. The DESG
Graduate Scheme is a carefully structured but flexible training programme;
enabling each graduate to get the most from a series of training courses and
work placements (including placements with industry).

Through this unique scheme each graduate is able to further their professional
development – making it possible for them to gain tremendous engineering or
science experience and to achieve Chartered status within just four years.

We have the technology

MINISTRY OF DEFENCE

We are: The Ministry of Defence,
Defence Engineering and Science Group:

Organisation description: Central Government.
The DESG is the community of thousands of Engineers
and Scientists within the Ministry of Defence.

DESG offers you many benefits including:

1. Probably the very best graduate development scheme
   for engineers and scientists available in the UK – fully
   accredited by IMechE, IET, ICE, RINA, IoP and RAes.

2. Huge investment in you. Over and above your salary,
   the investment in support of your personal professional
   development will be around £20,000 per year!

3. An accelerated path to Chartered status in your
   Engineering or Science profession.

Jobs available: Jobs related to chosen engineering
system anchors in Aerospace Systems, Estates and
Construction, Maritime Systems, Nuclear Systems,
Communications and Information Systems, Land Systems,
Weapons, Ordnance, Munitions and Explosives.

Work Locations:
MoD sites across the UK and sometimes abroad.

Degree Disciplines Required:

A multitude of engineering disciplines are required.
Also, science disciplines with an emphasis on Physics.
Please see www.desg.mod.uk (and click Graduate
Opportunities/Graduate Scheme/Graduate Fact Sheet
for details of the huge range of Degree Disciplines required).

Application procedure: On-line application
via our website www.desg.mod.uk (Click How To Apply).

Application Deadline: Visit our website www.desg.mod.uk
(and Click How To Apply/Application Dates).

Undergraduate Sponsorship:
We also offer Undergraduate Sponsorship
(please see our website and click
'Student Opportunities' for details).

The MoD is an Equal Opportunities Employer

DEFENCE ENGINEERING
AND SCIENCE GROUP

Morgan Stanley

www.morganstanley.com/careers/recruiting

Vacancies for around 250 graduates in 2009

- Finance
- Investment Banking
- IT

Vacancies also available in Europe, Asia and the USA.

Starting salary for 2009
£Competitive

Universities that Morgan Stanley plans to visit in 2008-9
Bath, Bristol, Cambridge, City, Durham, Edinburgh, London, Oxford, Warwick
Please check with your university careers service for details of events.

Application deadline
9th November 2008
See website for full details.

Contact Details
✉ graduaterecruitmenteurope@morganstanley.com

Turn to page 256 now to request more information or visit our new website at www.top100graduateemployers.com

Morgan Stanley is a leading global financial services firm providing a wide range of investment banking, securities, investment management and wealth management services.

The firm has over 45,000 employees in more than 600 offices in 33 countries, serving clients worldwide including corporations, governments, institutions and individuals. Their services include: investment banking advice on mergers and acquisitions, privatisations and financial restructuring; debt and equity underwriting; sales and trading in all the world's major markets; and market leading research. Morgan Stanley also manages more than $700 billion for institutional and high net worth investors across a broad range of asset classes, from traditional equity and fixed income through to hedge funds, private equity, real estate and infrastructure.

Analyst training at Morgan Stanley quickly makes effective professionals. Through a structured programme, graduates receive an intensive induction on how to use Morgan Stanley's unsurpassed data resources and analytic tools.

Graduates work on a team under the direct guidance of senior professionals who are among the best in their fields. They will give as much responsibility as graduates can handle, in an environment that affords exciting opportunities to work with a wide variety of clients in different industries, helping them to make strategic decisions involving capital raising, research or trading issues at the highest level. Training is not limited to the first weeks or months on the job but is ongoing throughout a career at Morgan Stanley.

Morgan Stanley accepts applications from all degree types. They are looking for candidates with a keen intellect, excellent communication skills, analytical aptitude and high dedication to their professional responsibilities.

NATIONAL GRADUATE
DEVELOPMENT PROGRAMME

ngdp.

FOR LOCAL GOVERNMENT

www.ngdp.co.uk

**Vacancies for around
80+ graduates in 2009**

■ General Management

REAL VALUE

REAL CHANGE

Starting salary for 2009
£25,301
With London weighting.
National salary rise pending.

The ngdp is a two-year graduate development programme, run by the Improvement and Development Agency (The IDeA) that is designed to develop future managers and leaders in local government.

It was set up to provide local government with the high calibre managers their communities need, and to give committed graduates the training, qualifications and opportunities to make a real difference. Local government is the largest employer in the UK, with over two million staff in over 400 local authorities and in excess of 500 different occupational areas.

**Universities that ngdp
plans to visit in 2008-9**
Please check with your university
careers service for details of events.

Over 300 graduates have completed the programme and many now hold important managerial and policy roles in the sector. Local government is going through many positive changes at present and as a trainee on the ngdp, graduates will be at the forefront of these changes.

The programme consists of placements in key areas of local authority service and offer a range of experiences designed to provide a broad understanding of many aspects of local government, including: strategy, service delivery and support service.

Application deadline
12th January 2009

Trainees will participate in the IDeA Graduate Leadership Academy, which combines study for a bespoke Postgraduate Diploma in Local Government Management at Warwick Business School with soft skill development training. Mentoring also provided on a regional basis and programme support is provided through a dedicated central ngdp team.

Contact Details
✉ enquiries@ngdp.co.uk
☎ 0845 222 0250

Turn to page 256 now to request more information or visit our new website at www.top100graduateemployers.com

Other graduate entry routes into local government can be found at www.LGtalent.com

NATIONAL GRADUATE DEVELOPMENT PROGRAMME

ngdp

FOR LOCAL GOVERNMENT

REAL CONCERNS

Crystal Clear Acrylic Coating

The **ngdp** is a graduate development programme run by the Improvement and Development Agency (IDeA). It's designed to provide local government with the high-calibre managers their communities need, and give committed graduates the training, qualifications and opportunities to make a real difference. Over two years you'll undertake a series of placements, covering front line services, support services and strategy. You'll receive a competitive salary and benefits. You'll also get to study for a fully funded post-graduate diploma, delivered through Warwick Business School. But most of all, you'll get the chance to see your ideas have real impact. To find out more, visit www.ngdp.co.uk or call 0845 222 0250 for a brochure.

Real life. Real work.

www.ngdp.co.uk

Vacancies for around 240 graduates in 2009

- Finance
- General Management
- Human Resources
- IT

Starting salary for 2009
£20,620

Universities that the NHS plans to visit in 2008-9

Aston, Bath, Birmingham, Bristol, Cambridge, East Anglia, Essex, Exeter, Hull, Keele, Kent, Lancaster, Leeds, Leicester, Liverpool, London, Loughborough, Manchester, Newcastle, Northumbria, Nottingham, Nottingham Trent, Oxford, Oxford Brookes, Sheffield, Southampton, Sussex, Warwick, York
Please check with your university careers service for details of events.

Application deadline
28th November 2008

Contact Details

✉ nhsgads@tmpw.co.uk

☎ 0845 300 1426

Turn to page 256 now to request more information or visit our new website at www.top100graduateemployers.com

Lead the way.

It's what we do.
It's what we want you to do.

What can be done to prevent half of the British population from becoming obese by 2050? How can Europe's largest single organisation reduce its impact on UK carbon emissions? How will the credit crunch affect the provision of healthcare services in the UK?

These are exactly the sort of questions managers in the NHS are tackling. And this award winning Graduate Management Training Scheme promises to give future managers the answers via comprehensive training and development essential to preparing this world-class organisation for the demands of the future.

Employing 1.3 million people and responsible for an annual budget of £100 billion – career opportunities really don't get much bigger than with the NHS. No other graduate scheme can offer the complexity, challenge, and sheer scope of being part of an organisation that looks after 60 million people from their very first breath.

Individuals can choose to join the NHS scheme in Finance, HR, General and Informatics Management, where they'll develop the skills essential to playing a leading role in the provision of world class, patient led healthcare, and attain postgraduate and professional qualifications. And with placements available across England, there's ample opportunity for individuals to impact on the NHS in their local area.

The NHS welcomes applicants from all backgrounds who have or are expecting at least a 2:2 degree. Postgraduates, mature students and those working within the NHS are encouraged to apply. Other qualifications may be accepted – please see the NHS website for eligibility criteria.

If we **catch a cold** when America sneezes,
what are the main side effects?

How will the panic in world financial markets affect the health of the nation? Will the 91% increase in oil prices have an effect on our supply of medicines? Will the higher cost of living lead to a lower standard of living? Join our Graduate Management Training Scheme and you'll be tackling questions just like these. With 1.3 million employees and a £100 billion budget, we're one of the world's largest and most innovative organisations, finding solutions to some of the country's biggest issues. Whatever your degree, our world-class development will give you the skills you need to lead and influence change, push the boundaries and help keep Britain – and the NHS – in good health.

NHS Leaders. Lead the way

 Graduate Management
Training Scheme

www.nhsgraduates.co.uk

Finance | General Management | HR | Informatics   Lead the way

npower

Vacancies for around 50 graduates in 2009

- Engineering
- Finance
- General Management
- IT

Starting salary for 2009
£25,000
Plus £2,000 golden hello.

Universities that npower plans to visit in 2008-9

Bath, Birmingham, Bristol, Cardiff, Durham, Lancaster, Leeds, Liverpool, Loughborough, Manchester, Newcastle, Nottingham, Sheffield, Southampton, Warwick
Please check with your university careers service for details of events.

Application deadline
See website for full details.

Contact Details
graduate.team@RWEnpower.com

Turn to page 256 now to request more information or visit our new website at www.top100graduateemployers.com

npower is one of the UK's leading integrated energy companies, and part of RWE, one of Europe's largest utility groups. As Britain's brightest energy company, npower gives creative and ambitious graduates the chance to work on exciting projects.

They operate one of the largest portfolios of power generating plants in the UK and supply electricity and gas to more than 6.8 million residential and business customers. And they are also one of the leaders in the search for renewable power sources, having developed the UK's first major offshore wind farm, and operating hydroelectric power stations in Scotland and Wales, using advanced communications and forecasting technology. They are committed to conducting their business with a sense of responsibility for the environment, their customers and for the communities in which they work.

As Britain's brightest energy company they are looking for Britain's brightest graduates. They have opportunities in engineering, general business management, finance, business analysis, risk and IS within RWE IT UK. npower will give those who bring enthusiasm, commitment, and the capacity to learn combined with strong analytic and problem-solving skills the opportunity to shine. npower's graduate programme will introduce successful applicants to the many different facets of their business, and give them responsibility at an early stage within their chosen area of work.

npower are committed to attracting and retaining the best, so all their graduates receive an excellent pay and benefits package which includes a competitive starting salary and 'golden hello' payment, and the salary is reviewed annually.

Who squeezes every drop
of goodness
out of their juice?

Who said that clean energy was just an electric dream?
At npower we've developed 'Juice' – greener electricity which
comes from renewable resources. Such as our very own
wind farms. These wind farms produce enough power to boil
nearly a billion kettles a year (give or take the odd peppermint
tea), and we don't charge our customers anything to switch over
to using it.

Because with us, it's not just about making sure the nation
can enjoy a nice cup of coffee. We need to think about the
environment and answer the questions that are fuelling the UK
energy agenda right now. Which is why we need some seriously
bright graduates to work on these issues from day one.
So whether you join us in engineering, general business
management, finance, business analysis, risk or IS within RWE IT
UK, we'll make sure the one question you're not asking is "do
you take sugar with that?".

Find out more about the energy company that won't go off the
boil by visiting **www.brightergraduates.com**

RWE Group

 Oxfam

Be Humankind

Vacancies for around 100 graduates in 2009

- Accountancy
- Finance
- General Management
- Human Resources
- IT
- Marketing
- Media
- Research & Development
- Retailing

These days, to save the world...

Starting salary for 2009
£Voluntary

Universities that Oxfam plans to visit in 2008-9
Please check with your university careers service for details of events.

Application deadline
Year-round recruitment

Contact Details
✉ internship@oxfam.org.uk

Turn to page 256 now to request more information or visit our new website at www.top100graduateemployers.com

There's only one super power that can help to win the fight against poverty and injustice. People power. Oxfam GB is a relief, development and campaigning organisation that combines the time and talents of more than a million staff, volunteers and supporters to make poverty history.

Forget tea rounds and shop runs. Oxfam's Voluntary Internship Scheme is planned around the precise needs of the organisation. Which means graduates have a significant impact on the projects and campaigns they work on. Whether they're helping to manage an Oxfam shop, plan and facilitate an Oxfam event, or keep the organisation running smoothly.

As a highly-valued member of the team, Oxfam interns should demonstrate a diverse range of talents including superb communication skills and the ability to influence the way people think. Naturally, commitment, enthusiasm and a genuine interest in the work Oxfam does are other important qualities.

Internships are based in Oxfam's retail shops, regional offices and Oxford headquarters. Graduates have the opportunity to volunteer with Oxfam for a period of three, six or twelve months, and although the work is unpaid, the scheme reimburses reasonable local travel and lunch expenses.

Few organisations can give graduates a genuine opportunity to make the world a better place. But Oxfam can. Joining a major international NGO, interns can expect to gain a thorough understanding of the scale and scope of the work Oxfam does – giving them the tools and experience they need to take their careers up, up and away.

...you don't need to wear your pants on the outside.

Voluntary Internship Opportunities UK-wide

Everyone at Oxfam is committed to fighting poverty and righting the wrongs in the world.

Be a hero and apply now (cape optional).

www.oxfam.org.uk/interns

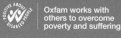

Oxfam works with others to overcome poverty and suffering.

Be Humankind

www.penguin.co.uk

Possible vacancies in 2009

- Accountancy
- Finance
- Human Resources
- Law
- Marketing
- Media
- Purchasing
- Sales

Starting salary for 2009
£19,620
Plus benefits.

Universities that Penguin plans to visit in 2008-9
Please check with your university careers service for details of events.

Application deadline
Year-round recruitment

Contact Details
Turn to page 256 now to request more information or visit our new website at www.top100graduateemployers.com

Words are just the beginning of Penguin Books' business, and for their people they're about so much more than what is seen on the page. Perhaps it's because for more than seventy years now they've been the publisher everyone looks to not just for great books, but also for innovation and for how to act with dignity and integrity.

They're always looking for different points of view, new voices and ways of working – and they're always happy to listen to new ideas. Which is why they have publishing's first green committee and diversity panel; why they have the leading publisher blog, podcast and website; and why last year they won all the major UK literary prizes as well as the Sales and Marketing 'Nibbie' for the second successive year – and ultimately why they were crowned Publisher of the Year at the 2007 British Book Awards.

They have opportunities for accountants, designers, publicists, marketers, production controllers, sales, rights and operations people – oh and for editorial and publishing staff, too. And with the Penguin family including Dorling Kindersley, Rough Guides, Puffin, Ladybird and Fredrick Warne, located in offices from London to the US, Australia, India and New Zealand, they're always looking for people prepared to think big.

No one is doing more to move publishing forward in the twenty-first century than Penguin. Facing the challenges of the digital revolution and ensuring that books of all shapes and sizes remain the cornerstone of a thriving culture will take some smart thinking and some innovative solutions – and not a few good words.

10

REASONS TO
BECOME A PENGUIN

1) **You get to work closely with your favourite authors.** Now what could be more fun than that? **2)** **We're a diverse bunch.** And we think publishing should be for everyone. **3)** **We're the greenest publishers in town.** We work with the Woodland Trust and our books are printed on FSC accredited paper. **4)** **Our award-winning publishing.** In 2006 we won the Man Booker, Orange and Whitbread prizes. **5)** **We know how to celebrate.** Our birthday parties and anniversary publishing have become the stuff of legend. **6)** **To prove publishing isn't stuffy we play at the cutting edge of the digital revolution.** Look us up at www.penguin.co.uk, find us in Second Life and come and have a chat with us on our blog. **7)** **People pay attention to what we do.** They just do. They can't help it. **8)** **We're the only publishing company in here.** Go on, check, but don't forget to come back here and finish the list. **9)** **You never need to explain what your company does at parties.** When you say 'I work for Penguin', everyone gets just a little bit jealous. **10)** **Your mum and dad will love you forever ...** (at least that's what our mums and dads tell us).

PUBLISHER
OF THE YEAR
2 0 0 7

CELEBRATE WITH US AT:
www.penguincelebrations.com

COULD YOU?
POLICE

Vacancies for unlimited **graduates in 2009**

■ All sectors

Starting salary for 2009
£24,000
On completion of training,
plus extensive benefits.

**Universities that HPDS
plans to visit in 2008-9**
Please check with your university
careers service for details of events.

Application deadline
Year-round recruitment

Contact Details
✉ hpds@npia.pnn.police.uk
☎ 020 7021 7070

Turn to page 256 now to request more
information or visit our new website at
www.top100graduateemployers.com

A career in the police offers an exciting mix of challenge and
reward. Policing in today's modern service involves reducing
crime and the fear of crime, working in partnership with the
public, supporting victims and witnesses whilst using the latest
technology to assist with the detection and prevention of crime.

The challenges faced by police officers are often mental rather than physical,
requiring an understanding of what makes people behave as they do, and to
use that knowledge to form strong policing skills. The modern police force
offers careers with many opportunities to enter specialist roles; traffic, fraud,
Criminal Investigation Department (CID), Special Branch (combating terrorism
and other serious crime), dog handlers and mounted officers, are just a few.

There are also great prospects to move up the career ladder into senior
leadership positions. Graduates from any discipline who have secured
employment as a police officer with one of the forces in England, Northern
Ireland or Wales may then be eligible to apply to join the Police High Potential
Development Scheme (HPDS). HPDS provides development opportunities
and structured support aimed at broadening members' experience of the
police service, and preparing them for strategic leadership roles.

The police offers a starting salary of around £21,500 p.a. upon joining,
rising to around £24,000 p.a. on completion of the initial training (salaries for
Metropolitan Police and City of London Police attract a London Weighting
supplement of around £6,000). The HPDS is funded by the National Policing
Improvement Agency (NPIA). Go to www.npia.police.uk for more information
about the NPIA.

POLICE PLEASE CROSS

We Challenge You

Every single day in the police service is a challenge. We're looking for people of outstanding ability who meet those challenges.

Take the challenge of your lifetime, join the police.

PRICEWATERHOUSE COOPERS

Vacancies for around 1,200 graduates in 2009

- Accountancy
- Consulting
- Finance
- Law

Starting salary for 2009
£Competitive
Plus flexible benefits and an interest-free loan.

Universities that PricewaterhouseCoopers plans to visit in 2008-9
Please check with your university careers service for details of events.

Application deadline
Varies by function
See website for full details.

Contact Details
☎ 0800 100 2200 or
+44 (0)121 265 5852
Turn to page 256 now to request more information or visit our new website at www.top100graduateemployers.com

PricewaterhouseCoopers LLP (PwC) is the one firm for all talented graduates. As one of the world's largest professional services firms they have a lot to offer. Exciting opportunities, with an enviable range of clients – from public and private companies to governments and charities – with whom we work in partnership to create leading-edge solutions.

Whether the degree is art or science related, PricewaterhouseCoopers offer breadth of career opportunity where graduates can build on the skills and experience they've gained at university, and develop their career. They expect a 2:1 and at least a 280 UCAS tariff or equivalent. But just as important are the personal qualities, enthusiasm and ideas graduates bring.

PwC offer a wide range of possibilities within their business groups, each of which boasts an eye-catching client list. Some of their groups are renowned as breeding grounds for the best business minds in their field. Others are at the forefront of developments in the challenging e-business arena.

Wherever successful applicants join they'll need to be prepared to work hard from day one and in return they will benefit from the development experience PwC invest in their people together with the breadth that the variety of work they can offer. In return for talent and commitment, they pay a competitive salary and have an innovative flexible benefits scheme.

To find out more about the opportunities on offer and to apply online, please visit – pwc.com/uk/careers/

FLEX**1**BLE
FOR ALL

Assurance
Tax
Advisory
Actuarial
Consulting

Requirements:
2:1 in any subject
280 UCAS tariff
or equivalent

Nationwide Opportunities Spring and Autumn 2009

No rigid thinking here. For instance, we've designed our structured development programmes to fit around you – whether you want to specialise in one specific business area or gain a broad experience. We encourage you to think laterally, as well as logically, wherever you work. And we even offer a benefits package you can tailor to your specific needs. We also look forward to seeing what you have to offer. If you're as flexible as we are, you could soon be finding out first-hand why, **for the fifth year running, we've been voted number one in the Times Top 100 Graduate Employers survey for offering the greatest opportunity**. There's only one number one employer – so find out why we're the one firm for all adaptable graduates.

pwc.com/uk/careers/

Text: PwC to 85792

(Texts charged at your standard network rate.)

PRICEWATERHOUSE COOPERS

We value diversity in our people.

P&G

Vacancies for around 60 graduates in 2009

- Engineering
- Finance
- Human Resources
- IT
- Logistics
- Manufacturing
- Marketing
- Purchasing
- Research & Development
- Sales

Vacancies also available in Europe.

Starting salary for 2009
£Competitive

Universities that Procter & Gamble plans to visit in 2008-9

Aston, Bath, Birmingham, Bristol, Cambridge, Cardiff, Dublin, Durham, Edinburgh, Glasgow, Lancaster, Leeds, London, Loughborough, Manchester, Newcastle, Nottingham, Oxford, Southampton, St Andrews, Strathclyde, Warwick, York
Please check with your university careers service for details of events.

Application deadline
Year-round recruitment

Contact Details
✉ recunitedkingdm.im@pg.com

Turn to page 256 now to request more information or visit our new website at www.top100graduateemployers.com

Established 170 years ago, P&G is the most admired Household and Personal Goods company in the world. It has one of the largest and strongest portfolios of trusted, quality brands, including Ariel, Always, Braun, Crest, Duracell, Gillette, Head&Shoulders, Iams, Lenor, Olay, OralB, Pampers, Pantene and Pringles.

Every day these brands touch the lives of more than three billion people around the world. 140,000 P&G people in 80 countries worldwide work to ensure P&G brands live up to their promise to make everyday life a little better.

P&G attracts and recruits the finest people in the world, because it grows and develops its senior managers within the organisation. This means new starters with P&G can expect a job with responsibility from day one and a career with a variety of challenging roles that develop and broaden their skills, together with the support of training and coaching to help them succeed.

P&G offers exciting careers in all the functions required to operate a major multinational company. These include Customer Business Development (sales & commercial careers), Finance, Human Resources, Information Decisions & Solutions (careers adding value to their business processes through IT), Marketing (careers in brand management), Product Supply (careers in engineering, purchasing, manufacturing and supply chain management) and Research and Development.

The company looks for talented graduates with a broad range of skills demonstrated through their activities and interests. Most functions welcome applicants from any degree discipline, Product Supply requires an engineering degree and R&D requires an engineering or science degree.

challenge

Are you ready to face a new challenge every day?

A career with Procter & Gamble offers roles with real responsibility from day one with the training and coaching to help you succeed. With $23 billion brands and operations across 80 countries, you will find your work really does bring a new challenge every day!

Add to this P&G's approach to growing our top leadership within the organisation and you will understand why your continuing development is so important to our success.

If you are ready for this challenge then we are ready for you! Apply online at **www.pgcareers.com** for vacancies throughout Europe.

- CBD/Sales
- Marketing
- Product Supply
- Research & Development

- Finance & Accounting
- Human Resources
- Information and Decision Solutions

To find out more visit  www.PGcareers.com

P&G a new challenge every day

QinetiQ

Vacancies for around
150 graduates in 2009

- Engineering
- IT

Starting salary for 2009
£Competitive

Universities that QinetiQ
plans to visit in 2008-9

Bath, Birmingham, Bristol,
Durham, Exeter, Glasgow,
Liverpool, London,
Loughborough, Manchester,
Nottingham, Oxford,
Sheffield, Southampton,
Strathclyde, Surrey,
Warwick, York
Please check with your university
careers service for details of events.

Application deadline
31st December 2008

Contact Details
☎ 08700 100 942

Turn to page 256 now to request more
information or visit our new website at
www.top100graduateemployers.com

QinetiQ believes that if a mind is agile enough, it can achieve just about anything. QinetiQ creates incredible solutions to seemingly insurmountable problems. Then they transform those solutions into a whole range of even more astounding commercial applications.

So a signal processing system designed for the defence arena becomes a revolutionary foetal heart monitor. A material developed to sound-proof helicopters becomes flat panel speakers. And stealth bomber technology helps to build wind farms.

A world-renowned defence, technology and security company, QinetiQ offers a broad range of careers covering operational analysis, scientific research, development, test and evaluation and project management – in fields ranging from media to healthcare, aerospace to security and telecoms to transport.

QinetiQ is a unique organisation seeking 150 extraordinary new people a year. They look for proactive, analytical, forward-thinking graduates from most science, engineering, IT and numerate disciplines.

QinetiQ offers a good salary and benefits package combined with real quality of life – the chance to do fascinating work in a pleasant environment. Their people are given the freedom, resources and training they need to push the boundaries of existing knowledge. Working alongside some of the leading people in their field, there are remarkable development opportunities.

In December 2008, QinetiQ will be using their world-beating science and technology to support Ben Fogle and James Cracknell's Team QinetiQ in the Amundsen Omega 3 South Pole Race.

QinetiQ

HOW DO YOU GO
FROM FRONTLINE
TO POLE POSITION?

Calculating the computational fluid dynamics behind the design
of a 21st century fighter jet is clever. Transforming the same expertise
into the design of a Formula 1 or Le Mans car, that's QinetiQ clever.

Science, engineering and technology graduates can join the real
transformers at **http://graduates.QinetiQ.com**

Rolls-Royce

www.rolls-royce.com/university

Vacancies for around 160+ graduates in 2009

■ Engineering

Starting salary for 2009
£Competitive

Universities Rolls-Royce plans to visit in 2008-9
Please check with your university careers service for details of events.

Application deadline
Year-round recruitment

Contact Details
✉ HRSharedServiceCentre@ Rolls-Royce.com
☎ 01332 333333

Turn to page 256 now to request more information or visit our new website at www.top100graduateemployers.com

It's no wonder that graduates are proud to work for Rolls-Royce, as they contribute to a variety of exciting projects that power the world we live in.

As an engineering company renowned for its technological excellence, Rolls-Royce is a global market leader in the highly competitive civil aerospace, defence aerospace, marine and energy sectors, developing innovative solutions to address today's burning issues. Issues such as how to meet the world's demand for air travel, while reducing its effect on the environment.

Graduates face some of the most challenging business scenarios imaginable. It's a highly competitive world that requires the best supply chain, the strongest finance operation, the most creative deal-makers, the best-organised project managers, the greatest customer focus and the finest engineers. There are two graduate programmes on offer. The Professional Excellence Programme enables graduates to become a recognised expert in a particular field. The Leadership Development Programme focuses on developing leadership skills within a function.

These programmes challenge, stretch and enthuse graduates from a range of backgrounds. Tailored to meet the graduate's individual needs, they enable them to perform to their full potential through a combination of job experience, formal training, project work and a variety of other activities.

With 38,000 employees around the world, the company aims to make a positive contribution to the communities they operate in. This means graduates enjoy the chance to work closely with colleagues in a variety of countries and are encouraged to get involved in a range of community-based projects.

"Today I powered a different kind of thinking."
What will you do tomorrow?

Engineering • Finance • Supply Chain • Purchasing • Operations Management • HR • Commercial • Customer Management • Marketing • Project Management

Graduate opportunities

It's no wonder our graduates are proud to work for us. From developing aircraft engines that produce lower emissions, ship engines that run on liquefied gas and compression systems that move 12 million m³ of gas an hour, to negotiating with major suppliers and customers, they contribute to a variety of exciting projects that power the world we live in.

Join us and you'll discover that we're leading the way in the civil and defence aerospace, energy and marine sectors. Whether you want to develop your professional expertise or your leadership ability, our graduate programmes are designed to meet your needs in a variety of business areas. So, what will you do tomorrow? To find out more about the opportunities on offer, just visit www.rolls-royce.com/university

Trusted to deliver excellence

www.rolls-royce.com/university

 Rolls-Royce

Vacancies for around 700 graduates in 2009

- Engineering
- General Management
- Human Resources
- IT
- Law
- Logistics

Vacancies also available in Europe and the USA.

Starting salary for 2009
£28,216+

Universities that the Royal Air Force plans to visit in 2008-9

Aberdeen, Aberystwyth, Aston, Bangor, Bath, Belfast, Birmingham, Bradford, Bristol, Brunel, Cambridge, Cardiff, City, Dublin, Dundee, Durham, East Anglia, Edinburgh, Essex, Exeter, Glasgow, Heriot-Watt, Hull, Keele, Kent, Lancaster, Leeds, Leicester, Liverpool, London, Loughborough, Manchester, Newcastle, Northumbria, Nottingham, Nottingham Trent, Oxford, Oxford Brookes, Plymouth, Reading, Sheffield, Southampton, St Andrews, Stirling, Strathclyde, Surrey, Sussex, Swansea, Ulster, Warwick, York
Please check with your university careers service for details of events.

Application deadline
Year-round recruitment

Contact Details

☎ 0845 605 5555

Turn to page 256 now to request more information or visit our new website at www.top100graduateemployers.com

The Royal Air Force is the flying arm of the UK's Armed Forces. It offers a range of careers suitable for graduates, over a wide range of disciplines, from engineers to air traffic controllers and doctors to nurses.

To be selected for officer training, candidates must demonstrate that they have certain basic personal attributes that appropriate training can develop; these include the potential to use initiative effectively, make decisions under pressure and lead by example.

When graduates join the RAF, they begin their careers with the 30-week Initial Officer Training course at the RAF College Cranwell in Lincolnshire – although specialists undertake a shorter course; most newly-commissioned officers graduate in the rank of Flying Officer. A period of professional training follows, the length of which varies from branch to branch. Promotion to Flight Lieutenant is on a time and satisfactory service basis – usually awarded within a couple of years; advancement beyond that is by competitive selection based on annual appraisals.

On successful completion of professional training, officers begin their first productive tour. For ground branch officers this normally lasts for about 18 months; aircrew tours tend to be longer. RAF operations and exercises may be conducted in the UK or overseas; accordingly, all officers must be prepared to serve anywhere in the world.

An RAF officer career demands high standards and commitment. In return the RAF offers high rewards; excellent career prospects, competitive salaries, a good pension scheme, free healthcare, ongoing professional and personal development training, and many opportunities for travel, sport and adventure.

RAF Officer. Rise to the challenge.

As an Officer in the RAF you'll be part of a key team of skilled managers from the outset, responsible for the smooth running of an organization that's bigger and more complex than many businesses. You'll also get professional training and qualifications (like your civilian peers) and be rewarded accordingly. And with over 50 careers to choose from you don't have to be a pilot to fly with us. If you've got an appetite for adventure, ambition and team spirit, then the sky's the limit.

To see your career take off visit rafcareers.com

◎ ROYAL AIR FORCE

The Royal Bank of Scotland Group

**Vacancies for around
600+ graduates in 2009**

- Accountancy
- Finance
- General Management
- Human Resources
- Investment Banking
- IT
- Marketing
- Purchasing
- Retailing
- Sales

Vacancies also available in Europe, Asia, the USA and elsewhere in the world.

Starting salary for 2009
£26,450-£46,000

**Universities that
The Royal Bank of
Scotland Group
plans to visit in 2008-9**

Aberdeen, Aston, Bath, Belfast, Birmingham, Bristol, Cambridge, Cardiff, City, Dublin, Durham, Edinburgh, Exeter, Glasgow, Heriot-Watt, Lancaster, Leeds, London, Loughborough, Manchester, Newcastle, Nottingham, Oxford, Reading, Sheffield, Southampton, St Andrews, Strathclyde, Warwick, York
Please check with your university careers service for details of events.

Application deadline
Varies by programme
See website for full details.

Contact Details
✉ rbsgrads@tmpw.co.uk

Turn to page 256 now to request more information or visit our new website at www.top100graduateemployers.com

The Royal Bank of Scotland Group doesn't stand still. By combining acquisition with organic growth, they have grown at a pace. They entered US banking with the acquisition of Citizens Bank which is now the ninth largest bank in the US ranked by both assets and deposits. In 2007, as part of a consortium, they acquired ABN AMRO in the largest banking transaction ever.

The RBS group is now a truly global bank, with a presence in the economies that account for 91% of global GDP growth. With over 40 brands including NatWest, RBS, Mint, Ulster Bank Group and Coutts & Co, they are making it happen for more than 40 million customers in over 50 countries and 170,000 employees worldwide.

RBS has over 600 graduate opportunities, ranging from Finance and Risk to Corporate Banking, and from Marketing to Human Resources. They also run a number of internships, to give students a real taste of life at one of the world's largest financial services groups.

As one might expect from a group their size, graduates will be supported via a network of buddies and mentors as well as formal and on-the-job training. They will also have the opportunity to continue studying for professional qualifications or take part in group-funded community programmes.

Graduates will need a 2:1 or 2:2 depending on programme in any discipline – combined with the focus and tenacity to deliver in a truly global organisation. The salaries quoted include 15% pension which is flexible and can be used as cash and/or contributions plus joining bonus, location allowance (if applicable), discretionary performance bonus, profit sharing and other excellent benefits.

We've got over 50 countries for you to get stuck into.

50 countries. 50 cultures. Countless opportunities to take your career further. And it's not just our geographical spread that makes The Royal Bank of Scotland Group such an exciting place to launch your career. With over 30 graduate programmes in everything from Retail Business Leadership, Property and Purchasing to Global Markets, Technology Services and Audit, there's something for everyone, whatever degree discipline and career aspiration. Ready to make it happen? Then find out more at **www.makeitrbs.com**

Make it happen™

LIFE WITHOUT LIMITS

ROYAL NAVY

royalnavy.mod.uk/careers

Vacancies for no fixed quota **of graduates in 2009**

- Engineering
- Finance
- General Management
- Human Resources
- IT
- Law
- Logistics
- Research & Development

Starting salary for 2009
£28,216-£31,188

Universities that the Royal Navy plans to visit in 2008-9

Aston, Bath, Belfast, Birmingham, Bristol, Brunel, Cardiff, Durham, Edinburgh, Exeter, Glasgow, Heriot-Watt, Leeds, Leicester, London, Loughborough, Manchester, Newcastle, Northumbria, Nottingham, Plymouth, Sheffield, Southampton, Strathclyde, Surrey, Swansea, Ulster, Warwick, York
Please check with your university careers service for details of events.

Application deadline
Year-round recruitment

Contact Details
☎ 08456 07 55 55

Turn to page 256 now to request more information or visit our new website at www.top100graduateemployers.com

For final year students and graduates, a life-changing career with the Royal Navy really could be just a few months away and, after a few years, the chances are that successful applicants will have seen more of the world than most people ever do – and acquired a set of skills to last a lifetime.

The Royal Navy is a modern and forward-thinking organisation operating globally at sea, ashore and in the air to protect UK interests worldwide. Its role includes maritime law enforcement, search-and-rescue operations and humanitarian relief in disaster areas. It enforces sanctions as an aid to diplomacy, prevents conflict and, if necessary, takes decisive military action.

Employing 37,000 personnel in locations across the globe, the Royal Navy offers graduates a wide variety of rewarding and challenging careers: from Engineering and Mechanics to Combat Operations and Dentistry; Aircrew and Air Operations Support to Logistics and Information Technology.

Graduates start on a starting salary of at least £28,216, plus a joining bonus upon entry (dependent on branch specialisation). For example, final year students and graduates of ECUK (Engineering Council UK) accredited engineer disciplines who join as Engineer Officers receive a £12,000 joining bonus.

Whatever branch successful applicants choose provides early management responsibilities, opportunities for promotion, professional accreditation and importantly, excellent job security. Then of course, there is the amazing travel and adventure that comes with the job, plus discounted travel costs, exceptional sporting facilities and an exciting social life.

Graduates are sought on a continuous basis. Have a look at royalnavy.mod.uk/careers for information on the variety of roles available.

ROYAL NAVY ENGINEER:
TODAY YOU'LL JUST BE WORKING ON A FAN

The fan just happens to be at the front of a 26,150 shaft horsepower Spey gas turbine. It powers the Royal Navy's Type 23 Frigates through the water at speeds of 30 knots.

As a Royal Navy Engineer you'll train faster and go further. It's an important role, where your diagnosis and decisions will affect the ship's operational capabilities and effectiveness.

If you want more than just a job, join the Royal Navy and live a life without limits.

£12,000 joining bonus
Salary: £28,216-£74,023pa*
Train faster & go further

JOIN THE ROYAL NAVY
VISIT ROYALNAVY.MOD.UK/CAREERS
OR CALL 08456 07 55 55

ROYAL NAVY

LIFE WITHOUT LIMITS

*Graduates will start on a salary of £28,216 and could earn up to £74,023 as a General Service Commander. There is extra pay for those who qualify as Submariners.

Sainsbury's

Vacancies for around 75 graduates in 2009

- Human Resources
- IT
- Logistics
- Marketing
- Purchasing
- Retailing

Starting salary for 2009
£23,000-£25,000

Universities Sainsbury's plans to visit in 2008-9

Aston, Bath, Bristol, Exeter, Lancaster, Leeds, Leicester, Loughborough, Manchester, Newcastle, Northumbria, Nottingham, Reading, Sheffield, Warwick

Please check with your university careers service for details of events.

Application deadline

Varies by function

Early application is advised. Please see website for full details.

Contact Details

☎ 0845 603 6290

Turn to page 256 now to request more information or visit our new website at www.top100graduateemployers.com

Sainsbury's is a leading FTSE 100 company and a very high-profile name in a fast-moving market. The success of their recently completed 'Making Sainsbury's Great Again' review, has seen the company's sales grown by £2.7b and profits double. Their plans continue at pace to improve the customer shopping experience.

Sainsbury's needs bright, savvy people, who love the buzz of retail and are hungry for success. They want exceptionally motivated and creative people ready to add value to the business. One of Sainsbury's key values is 'respect for the individual' which supports their culture of ensuring that everyone feels valued and respected in everything they do.

The organisation's Retail scheme aims to develop sucessful applicants into a Deputy Store Manager at one of their Centres of Excellence around the country. The expansion of Non-Food in Coventry has created opportunities in Non-Food Buying, Merchandising and Product Technology. There are also opportunities based in the London Store Support Centre in Customer and Marketing, Logistics IT, Buying (Food), Product Technology (Food), Product Development (Food), Human Resources, IT, Commercial, Location Planning and Property. Please see the website for summer and one year placements.

An essential element to all schemes is a four to six-month store placement. This is a real business that runs on getting the basics right, and there's no better place to learn that than out in a busy store.

But first things first: find out more about what makes a business like Sainsbury's tick at www.sainsburys.co.uk/graduates

Vacancies for around 300 graduates in 2009

- Engineering
- Finance
- Human Resources
- IT

Vacancies also available in Europe.

Starting salary for 2009
£30,250
Including benefits.

Universities that Shell plans to visit in 2008-9

Aberdeen, Bath, Birmingham, Bristol, Cambridge, Durham, Edinburgh, Heriot-Watt, Leeds, London, Loughborough, Manchester, Nottingham, Oxford, Sheffield, Strathclyde, Warwick
Please check with your university careers service for details of events.

Application deadline
Year-round recruitment

Contact Details

✉ graduates@shell.com

☎ 0845 600 1819

Turn to page 256 now to request more information or visit our new website at www.top100graduateemployers.com

Pursue it

A more exciting
career experience

Achieving more together

Shell is at the heart of the energy and petrochemical business and is one of the world's most successful organisations. They are totally committed to a business strategy that always balances profits with principles. They are also committed to attracting, training, developing and rewarding world class people for this truly world class business.

From the moment graduates join Shell, their development is of prime importance. Learning by doing, supported by their manager, is key – real responsibility and decision-making are part of life at Shell from day one. Career progression depends entirely on individual ability, talent and ambition.

Working for Shell, graduates could potentially move geographically, functionally and between different businesses. Shell have a strong ethic of promotion from within, supported by a global job opportunity intranet site.

Graduates' academic records are one key factor in assessing applications, but Shell also place emphasis on performance during interviews and assessment centres. Shell have identified capacity, achievement and relationships as critical to high performance.

Shell have a number of pre-employment opportunities: the Shell Gourami Business Challenge, for which applications are welcome from students who will be in their final year when Gourami takes place; the Personal Development Award, for which applications are welcome from non-finalists.

Full details on Shell can be found on their website, www.shell.com/careers

Shell people aren't all the same

IDEAS PEOPLE WANTED
CAREERS AT SHELL

And we like it that way. After all, the more different perspectives we have on board, the more great ideas we can come up with.

With a presence in more than 110 countries, we've learned for ourselves that being an inclusive business is an advantage. Now we're looking for more people who share our thinking.

So if you want to achieve more in your career, get together with Shell at **shell.com/careers** and quote reference GAL311G when applying.

Shell is an Equal Opportunity Employer.

sky

www.sky.com/jobs

Vacancies for around 55 graduates in 2009

- Finance
- General Management
- IT
- Marketing

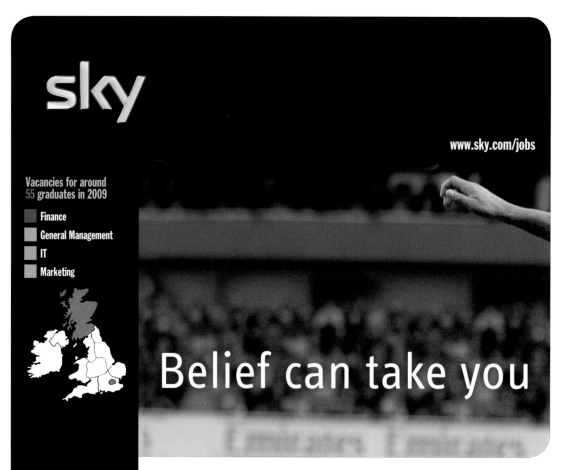

Belief can take you

Starting salary for 2009
£Competitive

Universities that Sky plans to visit in 2008-9
Bath, Birmingham, Bristol, Cambridge, Cardiff, Durham, Edinburgh, Glasgow, Heriot-Watt, London, Loughborough, Manchester, Nottingham, Oxford, Strathclyde, Warwick
Please check with your university careers service for details of events.

Application deadline
31st December 2008

Contact Details
Turn to page 256 now to request more information or visit our new website at www.top100graduateemployers.com

By believing in better, Sky has put its FTSE 50 media and technology business at the leading edge of the industry. It's a business they've built by not only believing in being first for their customers, but also first with ground-breaking content and technology.

Sky's four graduate schemes offer comprehensive training, lots of scope for development and funding to gain a recognised professional qualification.

Then there's the responsibility – with graduates having the chance to be involved with some of Sky's most interesting projects. Recently, graduates have worked on financing deals with third parties, marketing the Hay Festival, designing interactive content for Sky News and creating an enhanced booking system for Sky+ installation. Plenty more examples can be found on the Sky website.

Sky not only delivers some of the most diverse content and services on the planet, they value the same diversity within their business – providing a culture of entrepreneurialism and opportunity for one and all.

Confident communicators, creative problem solvers and natural team players will fit right into Sky's exceptionally creative and fun environment. It's one in which there are no boundaries to what can be achieved and where the ability to innovate is far more important than any particular degree discipline. Sky is a business driven by fresh thinking and bright ideas.

Above all, Sky graduates must believe they've the potential to go far with a world-class team of professionals in one of the UK's most exciting businesses. For more information go to www.sky.com/jobs

a long way

Sky Future Talent

Amazing performances take a lot of belief.
Belief in yourself. In your abilities.
Above all, in your potential.

sky

Believe in better

SKY SPORTS

SLAUGHTER AND MAY

Vacancies for around 95 graduates in 2009
For training contracts starting in 2011

■ Law

Starting salary for 2009
£38,000

Universities that Slaughter and May plans to visit in 2008-9
Birmingham, Bristol, Cambridge, Dublin, Durham, Edinburgh, London, Manchester, Nottingham, Oxford, Warwick
Please check with your university careers service for details of events.

Application deadline
Year-round recruitment

Contact Details
✉ trainee.recruit@ slaughterandmay.com
Turn to page 256 now to request more information or visit our new website at www.top100graduateemployers.com

Slaughter and May is a leading international law firm whose principal areas of practice are in the fields of corporate, commercial and financing law.

The firm's clients range from the world's leading multinationals to venture capital start-ups. They include public and private companies, governments and non-governmental organisations, commercial and investment banks. The lawyers devise solutions for complex, often transnational, problems and advise some of the world's brightest business minds.

Their overseas offices and close working relationships with leading independent law firms in other jurisdictions mean there are opportunities to work in places such as Auckland, Brussels, Berlin, Copenhagen, Düsseldorf, Frankfurt, Helsinki, Hong Kong, Luxembourg, Madrid, Milan, New York, Oslo, Paris, Prague, Rome, Singapore, Stockholm, Sydney and Tokyo.

Approximately 95 training contracts are available per year for trainee solicitors. Slaughter and May also offers two-week work experience schemes at Christmas, Easter and during the summer for those considering a career in law.

Following Law School, there is a two year training period during which time trainee solicitors gain experience of a broad cross-section of the firm's practice by taking an active part in the work of four or five groups, sharing an office with a partner or experienced associate. In addition, Slaughter and May offers an extensive training programme of lectures, seminars and courses with discussion groups covering general and specialised legal topics.

Applications from candidates of good 2.1 ability from any discipline are considered. Please visit the website for further information.

SLAUGHTER AND MAY

GREAT MINDS THINK DIFFERENTLY

Slaughter and May is widely regarded as one of the most prestigious law firms in the world.

Our clients keep coming to us because we think and act differently. So what are we looking for in prospective trainees?

Forget all the clichés about who you know or where you went to university. If you have an enquiring mind, a good 2.1 degree (or better) not necessarily in law, and the ability to think for yourself, a career with Slaughter and May could be for you.

If you want to know more about training contracts and work experience schemes, go to: **slaughterandmay.com** or contact

The Trainee Recruitment Team
Slaughter and May
One Bunhill Row
London EC1Y 8YY
Tel: 020 7600 1200T +44 (0) 20 7600 1200

TeachFirst
LEARNING TO LEAD

Vacancies for around 460 graduates in 2009

■ All Sectors

Starting salary for 2009
£Competitive

CHANGE LIVES
INSPIRE A GENERATION

Universities Teach First plans to visit in 2008-9

Aston, Bath, Birmingham, Bristol, Cambridge, Cardiff, Durham, Edinburgh, Exeter, Lancaster, Leeds, Liverpool, London, Manchester, Newcastle, Nottingham, Nottingham Trent, Oxford, Sheffield, St Andrews, Warwick, York
Please check with your university careers service for details of events.

Application deadline
Winter: 5th December 2008
Final: 3rd April 2009
See website for full details.

Contact Details
✉ faq@teachfirst.org.uk

Turn to page 256 now to request more information or visit our new website at www.top100graduateemployers.com

Teach First is a unique two-year opportunity for graduates to be different and to achieve something special. Energy, intelligence and creativity can transform the futures of students in challenging schools around the UK. At the same time it's an opportunity to dramatically enhance individual career potential and to make a tangible difference to society.

Teach First takes exceptional graduates and transforms them into inspiring leaders – their leadership, inspiration and above all their example can be the key that unlocks the future of students confronted by a wide range of personal and social issues.

And while graduates are transforming the lives of young people in schools around the country, Teach First will help them to maximise their own potential. With high-quality training – leading to the achievement of Qualified Teacher Status – leadership development and supportive coaching and alumni programmes, Teach First will provide successful applicants with a strong platform of skills and experience to take forward into any future management career. That's why over 80 companies, government agencies and public bodies back Teach First to develop top talent for the future.

There is no question that Teach First is an extremely demanding option. After just six weeks graduates will be delivering real lessons to real students. But if Teach First is uniquely challenging, it is also uniquely satisfying. Few other options offer the same degree of genuine responsibility so early. And rarely, if ever, will graduates have the opportunity to make such a direct and important difference.

TESCO

Vacancies for around
250+ graduates in 2009

- Accountancy
- Consulting
- Engineering
- Finance
- Human Resources
- IT
- Law
- Logistics
- Marketing
- Media
- Purchasing
- Research & Development
- Retailing

Starting salary for 2009
£Competitive

Universities that Tesco
plans to visit in 2008-9

Aston, Bath, Bristol,
Cambridge, Cardiff,
Durham, Edinburgh,
London, Loughborough,
Manchester, Oxford,
Oxford Brookes, Reading,
Sheffield, Southampton,
Warwick
Please check with your university
careers service for details of events.

Application deadline
December 2008

Contact Details
✉ Graduate.recruitment@
uk.tesco.com

Turn to page 256 now to request more
information or visit our new website at
www.top100graduateemployers.com

Tesco is probably best known as the UK's number one retailer: a worldwide brand with a £51.7 billion turnover. But some will be unaware that the business is also a trail-blazer when it comes to greener retailing. For instance, Tesco's given out 1 billion fewer carrier bags since 2006.

But their commitment to the environment goes much further than that. Above is Tesco's first Express environmental store. It produces 31% less carbon and is on track for a reduction of 50%. Heating is provided by waste heat from the refrigeration units; rainwater is recycled; and walls are covered in wood from sustainable sources. Even the plants outside are drought tolerant.

So what does this innovation mean for graduates? Well it means they'll be joining a pioneering company that takes corporate social responsibility seriously – much like their people's development. Tesco's 17 graduate programmes range from Tesco.com, Property and Customer Analysis and Research in Head Office, to Stores and Distribution general management programmes (which have won the Times Graduate Employer of Choice award).

Depending on the area they join, graduates get involved in anything from sourcing and tasting prospective products, to negotiating prices with suppliers. From predicting sales forecasts for acquiring land, to developing board presentations. Within three to five years, graduates could even be running a depot or a store. In other words, Tesco's structured fast-track programme gives outstanding rewards and development.

Tesco is interested in graduates from every discipline with the drive to succeed: people who recognise the importance of delivering for the customer, whatever part of the business they work in.

Success.   # Sustained.

With 440,000 staff, stores in 13 countries and a total sales increase of over 50% during the past 5 years, it would be difficult to miss our business growth. Even our broccoli sales now weigh in at a staggering 450 tonnes a week in the UK!

But what may have passed you by is our growth as a green and sustainable business too. By getting our Tesco train on track delivering supplies, adopting re-usable trays saving 130,000 tonnes of cardboard and supporting farmers by buying local choice milk – we're cutting our CO_2 emissions more and more every day. Come and help us sustain our success, visit **www.tesco-graduates.com**

www.tesco-graduates.com

Tesco is an equal opportunities employer.

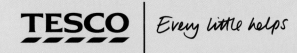

TESCO | *Every little helps*

THOMSON REUTERS

www.careers.thomsonreuters.com

Vacancies for around
40 graduates in 2009

- Accountancy
- Finance
- IT
- Marketing
- Media
- Sales

WHAT YOU DO HERE

Starting salary for 2009
£26,000-£27,500

Universities that
Thomson Reuters
plans to visit in 2008-9
Please check with your university
careers service for details of events.

Application deadline
31st December 2008

Contact Details
✉ graduate.recruitment@
thomsonreuters.com

Turn to page 256 now to request more
information or visit our new website at
www.top100graduateemployers.com

It is an exciting time to be part of Thomson Reuters. As the global leader in electronic information services, and related applications such as trading systems and news, they continually push the boundaries of information and technology. Their strong heritage and drive to innovate make Thomson Reuters a dynamic place to work.

It's a fascinating, challenging, fast-moving environment to work in – one that gives graduates a chance to make a real and immediate difference to the world around them.

There are four routes into Thomson Reuters for graduates. The Business programme is split into a number of placements within Thomson Reuters' functions and is designed to give graduates first-hand experience of how the company operates. On the Finance programme successful applicants get the best of both worlds – studying for the CIMA professional qualification while also gaining hands-on experience throughout the business. Technology drives everything Thomson Reuters does, so the Technology programme will put graduates right at the heart of the company where they'll work with truly world-class systems and products. The Thomson Reuters Journalism programme is one of the most sought-after training opportunities in the profession and will give graduates a chance to learn from the best in the business.

Whatever the programme, successful applicants will find themselves doing real work right from the start, exploring this incredibly diverse business and probably spending some time overseas. Longer term, they'll be encouraged to shape their own career development – and this is a company where they will never be short of options.

BE INFLUENTIAL FROM DAY ONE
JOIN AN ORGANISATION THAT
SHAPES DECISION-MAKING
AROUND THE WORLD

Transport for London

www.tfl.gov.uk/graduates

**Vacancies for around
123 graduates in 2009**

- Accountancy
- Engineering
- Finance
- General Management
- Human Resources
- IT
- Logistics
- Purchasing
- Research & Development

Starting salary for 2009
£24,000

**Universities that
Transport for London
plans to visit in 2008-9**
Please check with your university
careers service for details of events.

Application deadline
See website for full details.

Contact Details

✉ graduates@tfl.gov.uk

☎ 020 7957 7678

Turn to page 256 now to request more
information or visit our new website at
www.top100graduateemployers.com

Transport for London (TfL) are responsible for almost the entire London transport network. They manage everything from the London Underground and London Buses, to London Riverboat Services, London Trams and the Dockland's Light Railway. They also manage 580km of the Capital's roads, regulate taxis and work closely with the rail industry.

But they don't just get people from A to B. The services they deliver ensure the economic and social wellbeing of one of the world's greatest cities. In fact, London relies on the infrastructure and transport network that TfL provide. And not just for today – they are also playing a vital role in the preparation for the Olympic games, and in building a more sustainable future for the Capital.

They have recently secured a record £40bn settlement over ten years. This money will be used to improve and expand the network, and invested in some of the most exciting projects the Capital has ever seen. These include the continuation of the Oyster card scheme, (one of the world's largest electronic ticketing projects), low-carbon taxis, and some of the world's first hydrogen buses.

Supporting a population of 7 million people, not to mention the thousands of daily visitors, demands a team of nearly 23,000 people, in a vast range of roles. Which is why TfL offer an unprecedented variety of graduate schemes. In 2009 they have 123 placements on offer, in disciplines that include engineering, commercial, technical and general/project management.

We want to be as diverse as the city we represent and welcome applications from everyone regardless of age, gender, ethnicity, sexual orientation, faith or disability.

We are 1.8 billion annual passenger bus trips. We are 60 million

Docklands Light Railway journeys every year. We are 2.3 million

annual journeys on the River Thames. We are 80,000 licensed taxis

across London. We are 6,000 traffic lights. We are 580km of road

network. We are Transport for London. www.tfl.gov.uk/graduates

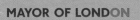

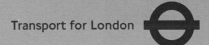

UBS

www.ubs.com/graduates

**Vacancies for around
500 graduates in 2009**

Finance

Human Resources

Investment Banking

IT

Marketing

Vacancies also available in Europe,
Asia, the USA and elsewhere in
the world.

Starting salary for 2009
£Competitive

**Universities that UBS
plans to visit in 2008-9**
Bristol, Cambridge, Durham,
London, Oxford, Warwick
Please check with your university
careers service for details of events.

Application deadline
2nd November 2008
See website for full details.

Contact Details
Turn to page 256 now to request more
information or visit our new website at
www.top100graduateemployers.com

UBS is one of the world's leading financial firms, serving a
discerning international client base. Its business, global
in scale, is focused on growth. As an integrated firm, UBS
creates added value for clients by drawing on the combined
resources and expertise of all its businesses.

UBS is the leading global wealth manager, a top tier investment banking and
securities firm, and one of the largest global asset managers. In Switzerland,
they are the market leader in retail and commercial banking.

UBS are present in all major financial centres worldwide. They have offices in
50 countries, with about 39% of its employees working in the Americas, 34% in
Switzerland, 17% in the rest of Europe and 10% in Asia Pacific. UBS's financial
businesses employ roughly 80,000 people around the world. Its shares are
listed on the SWX Swiss Stock Exchange, the New York Stock Exchange
(NYSE) and the Tokyo Stock Exchange (TSE).

It's true that building a career in financial services is a demanding option.
Successful applicants will good interpersonal skills, an ability to learn and
think quickly, alongside the determination to excel. The return on this
investment is a truly rewarding career with unlimited opportunities.

UBS are looking for graduates with a range of perspectives, experiences
and skills – people who can bring something different to the organisation.
Of course, academic credentials are important, but equally, demonstrable
communication skills, creativity, perseverance and tenacity. In return,
UBS offer excellent career opportunities designed to match graduates'
ambition and potential.

Together we...

can seize the moment.

At UBS every day is different and exciting – you could be working on any number and size of projects. So as part of a truly global team, you can take advantage of an environment that does not stand still. With your ideas making a genuine impact from day one, you can impress your peers, your managers and – most importantly of all – our clients. As one of the world's premier financial institutions, we can offer choice, opportunity and challenges to keep you on your toes. This is the ideal time to show us what you are made of.

It starts with you: www.ubs.com/graduates

UBS is an Equal Opportunity Employer. We respect and seek to empower each individual and the diverse cultures, perspectives, skills and experiences within our workforce.

Wealth Management | Global Asset Management | Investment Bank

You & Us

 UBS

Unilever

www.unilever.co.uk/careers

Vacancies for around 50 graduates in 2009

- Engineering
- Finance
- IT
- Marketing
- Research & Development
- Sales

We believe 'dirt is good.'
Not surprisingly we're looking
for people who aren't afraid
to get their hands dirty.

Starting salary for 2009
£26,000
Plus benefits.

Universities that Unilever plans to visit in 2007-8
Bath, Birmingham, Bristol,
Cambridge, Durham,
Edinburgh, Leeds, London,
Manchester, Nottingham,
Oxford, Sheffield, Warwick
Please check with your university
careers service for details of events.

Application deadline
January 2009
See website for full details.

Contact Details
✉ enquiry@
unilevergraduates.com
☎ 0870 154 3550
Turn to page 256 now to request more
information or visit our new website at
www.top100graduateemployers.com

Unilever is a leading consumer goods company, making and marketing products in the foods, home and personal care sectors across the world.

In fact over half the families in the world use brands such as Dove, Magnum, Knorr, Persil and Lynx every day. Unilever's mission is to add vitality to life – by helping people feel good, look good and get more out of life. Behind every successful brand lie a number of complex challenges, in all areas of the business: these are what graduates at Unilever will tackle.

Unilever's Graduate Leadership Programme is designed to help graduates reach senior management. Graduates join a specific function in Unilever, where they have a real job with key deliverables and responsibilities from the outset. Generally, the scheme includes four placements within two years therefore mobility is essential to achieve the breadth of experience required. There is excellent training covering leadership development, general business and professional skills. Full support is offered to gain Chartered status or relevant professional qualifications, such as CIMA, IMechE, IChemE and IEE.

Unilever wants people with the potential to lead its business. To do this, graduates need to be passionate about business, inspired by profit, competition and customer satisfaction, as well as have the ability to behave with integrity showing both ambition and entrepreneurial spirit. Unilever's high quality training programmes help graduates develop the expertise and personal qualities they need in order to achieve their career goals. They offer a vast range of opportunities that just have to be taken.

For more information, please visit www.unilever.co.uk/careers

Fancy a challenge?

Unilever Graduate Leadership Programme

At Unilever we're responsible for producing some of the world's most popular food, home and personal care brands. So if you've got a big appetite for success, you'll find our range of opportunities a truly mouth watering prospect.

Whether you join us in **Supply Chain, Marketing, Customer Development, Innovation & Technology Management, Financial Management** or **Information Technology** you'll benefit from world-class training; you'll gain a range of experience from up to four work placements; and you'll develop all the skills you need to become a future business leader.

So think: could you get stuck into the challenge of making well-loved brands like Lynx, Dove, Walls, Flora, Persil and Ben and Jerry's even more popular? Could you hold your own with some of the most talented, creative and inspirational people in the industry? If so, you could soon be looking forward to a exciting career. Hungry for more?

Visit www.unilever.co.uk/careers

Could it be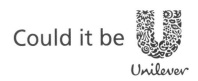

Watson Wyatt
Worldwide

Vacancies for around 90 graduates in 2009

- Consulting
- Finance
- Human Resources

What have you got in mind?

Starting salary for 2009
£26,000-£31,000

Universities that Watson Wyatt plans to visit in 2008-9

Bath, Bristol, Cambridge, City, Dublin, Durham, Heriot-Watt, Leeds, London, Manchester, Nottingham, Oxford, Southampton, St Andrews, Warwick, York
Please check with your university careers service for details of events.

Application deadline
7th November 2008

Contact Details
✉ graduate.recruitment@watsonwyatt.com

Turn to page 256 now to request more information or visit our new website at www.top100graduateemployers.com

Watson Wyatt is the trusted business partner to the world's leading organisations on people and financial issues. They advise over 70% of Fortune 500 Global companies headquartered in Britain and have 7,000 associates across 90 cities – from Mumbai to Melbourne, London to LA – but it is their client relationships, many spanning decades that define who they are.

They are experts in corporate governance, risk management and total reward, but providing graduates have the skills to build enduring client relationships, communicate complex information in simple language and provide perceptive insights and innovative solutions, they can teach successful applicants everything else they need to know.

The majority of their trainee positions are consulting roles and these roles fall into two categories – general (non-actuarial) and technical (actuarial) – and focus on one of three broad areas: Investment, Total Reward and Insurance.

The investment practice offers advice to institutional investors on all elements of investment strategy from the selection of fund managers to overall risk and liability management. They do not actively manage money, but are indirectly responsible for over 500 funds with assets worth more than $1 trillion.

They are renowned for expertise in the area of total reward and offer advice on all aspects of employee reward from strategic and executive compensation to the hot topic of pensions.

Their insurance practice offers technical advice to both Life and Non-Life Insurers, assisting with M&As, financial reporting, strategic planning, capital management, asset liability modelling, risk management and international accounting.

Watson Wyatt
Worldwide

On an edition of a popular daytime TV quiz show, the three contestants are asked to make a word found in the English dictionary from the following letters:

E E N P R S T

Once the 30 seconds are up, Dave, Michael and Jenny have all scored top marks with different seven-letter words. What were their answers?

Graduate Consultants

Mental challenges don't have to end with university. At least not at Watson Wyatt. Join us as a Consultant and you can expect all kinds of puzzles and conundrums as you apply your grey matter to advising some of the biggest names in business. Names that include over 70% of Fortune 500 Global companies headquartered in Britain.

Becoming part of a world-leading human capital and financial management consultancy won't be easy. That's why we invest in ambitious, logical graduates with impressive intellectual capabilities, top-notch communication skills and the drive to fulfil their true potential.

Still puzzled? Find all the answers at our website.

www.watsonwyatt.com/graduate

What have you got in mind?

WPP

**Vacancies for around
1-10 graduates in 2009**

Marketing

Media

Vacancies also available in the USA.

Starting salary for 2009
£Competitive

**Universities that WPP
plans to visit in 2008-9**
Bristol, Cambridge,
Durham, Edinburgh,
London, Nottingham,
Oxford, Warwick
Please check with your university
careers service for details of events.

Application deadline
19th November 2008

Contact Details
✉ hmiller@wpp.com
☎ 020 7408 2204

Turn to page 256 now to request more
information or visit our new website at
www.top100graduateemployers.com

WPP is one of the world's leading communications services
groups, made up of leading companies in advertising; media
investment management; information, insight & consultancy;
public relations & public affairs; branding & identity; healthcare
communications; direct, digital, promotion & relationship
marketing; and specialist communications.

WPP companies provide communications services to clients worldwide including
more than 340 of the Fortune Global 500; over half of the NASDAQ 100 and over
30 of the Fortune e-50. Collectively, WPP employs 110,000 people (including
associates) in over 2,000 offices in 106 countries.

WPP Marketing Fellowships, which develop high-calibre management talent
with experience across a range of marketing disciplines, will be awarded to
applicants who are intellectually curious and motivated by the prospect of
delivering high-quality communications services to their clients. All applicants
should have completed an undergraduate degree (class 2:1 or above)
or equivalent. Those selected will work in a number of WPP companies and
across different marketing disciplines.

WPP is offering several three-year Fellowships – a unique multi-disciplinary
experience, competitive remuneration and excellent long term career prospects
within WPP. It wants people who are committed to marketing, who take a
rigorous and creative approach to problem-solving, who are intellectually curious
and will function well in a flexible, loosely structured work environment.

Each year of the Fellowship is spent working in a WPP sponsoring company
and a personal mentor is assigned to provide career guidance. Each rotation is
chosen on the basis of the individual's interests and the Group's needs.

WPP

Marketing Fellowships 2009

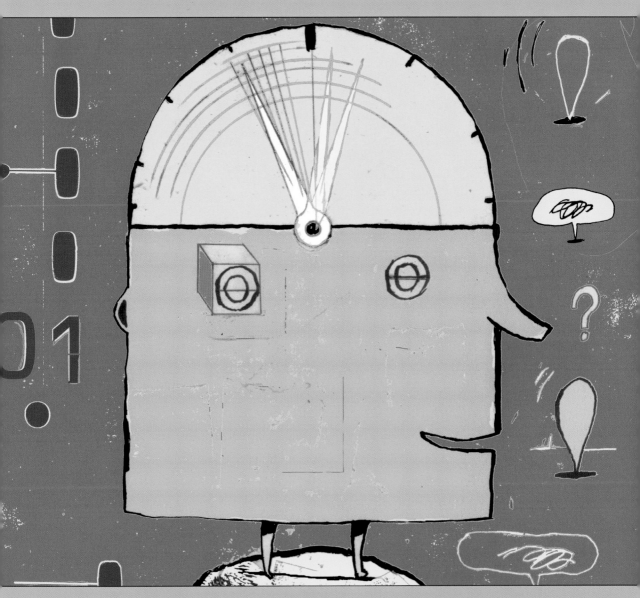

Ambidextrous brains required

WPP is one of the world's leading communications services groups. Major brands include JWT, Ogilvy & Mather Worldwide, Y&R, Grey, The Voluntarily United Group of Creative Agencies, MindShare, Mediaedge:cia, MediaCom, Millward Brown, Research International, KMR Group, OgilvyOne Worldwide, Wunderman, OgilvyAction, Hill & Knowlton, Ogilvy Public Relations Worldwide, Burson-Marsteller, Cohn & Wolfe, CommonHealth, Sudler & Hennessey, Ogilvy Healthworld, GHG, The Brand Union, Landor, Fitch and G2 among others.

Their specialist skills include Advertising; Media Investment Management; Information, Insight & Consultancy; Public Relations & Public Affairs; Branding & Identity; Healthcare Communications; Direct, Digital, Promotion & Relationship Marketing; and Specialist Communications. They are all in business to contribute to the success of their clients. And they do so through a demanding combination of flair and slog; intuition and logic; left brain and right brain.

We are looking for people who are intellectually curious and motivated by the prospect of delivering high-quality communications services to their clients. Those selected will work in a number of WPP companies and across different marketing disciplines. Excellent long-term career prospects within a WPP company.

Information leaflets are available from:
Harriet Miller at WPP, 27 Farm Street, London W1J 5RJ
T +44(0)20 7408 2204 F +44(0)20 7493 6819
E-mail: hmiller@wpp.com

Deadline for entry: 19 November 2008
visit our website and apply online at
www.wpp.com

Enter our prize draw to win

£5,000 in cash or a Nintendo DS Lite!

Make use of our free information service to find out more about the employers featured within this edition of **The Times Top 100 Graduate Employers,** and you could be £5,000 richer when you start your first job!

All you need to do is complete the special Top 100 **Information Request** card that appears opposite and send it back before the final closing date, **31st March 2009.**

Or you can register your details online at **www.Top100graduateemployers.com**

Every completed request card or online registration will be entered into a special prize draw to win £5,000 in cash.

There are also **50 Nintendo DS Lites** with **Dr. Kawashima's Brain Training** to be won – one at each of the universities at which the Top 100 book is distributed, for those who reply by **30th November 2008.**

The information that you request will be despatched to you from the Top 100 employers directly. This service is entirely free to all UK students and recent graduates.

Fill in the card or go to www.Top100GraduateEmployers.com now!

THE ✦ TIMES

TOP 100

GRADUATE EMPLOYERS

INFORMATION REQUEST 2008/2009

To request further information about any of the employers featured in The Times Top 100 Graduate Employers and enter our free prize draw to win £5,000, just complete your details and return this postcard.

Your information will be despatched to you directly from the employers, either by email, post or text message.

NAME _____

UNIVERSITY _____

COURSE _____

TERMTIME ADDRESS

_____

_____

_____

_____

EMAIL _____

MOBILE TEL. NO. _____

Please tick the sectors that you would most like to work in:

ACCOUNTANCY . . . . ❏
CONSULTING . . . . ❏
ENGINEERING . . . . ❏
FINANCE . . . . ❏
GENERAL MANAGEMENT . . . . ❏
HUMAN RESOURCES . . . . ❏
INVESTMENT BANKING . . . . . ❏
IT . . . . ❏
LAW . . . . ❏
LOGISTICS . . . . ❏
MANUFACTURING . . . . ❏
MARKETING . . . . ❏
MEDIA . . . . ❏
PURCHASING . . . . ❏
RESEARCH & DEVELOPMENT ❏
RETAILING . . . . ❏
SALES . . . . ❏

❏ PRE-FINAL YEAR   ❏ FINAL YEAR   ❏ I'VE ALREADY GRADUATED

The closing date to request information from these employers and be included in the prize draw to win £5,000 is **Tuesday 31st March 2009.** If you do **not** wish to be included on our general mailing list and receive information from other relevant graduate employers, please tick here ❏

Please tick the organisations you would like information from:

ACCENTURE . . . . ❏
ADDLESHAW GODDARD . . . . . . ❏
AIRBUS . . . . ❏
ALDI . . . . ❏
ALLEN & OVERY . . . . ❏
ARCADIA . . . . ❏
ARMY . . . . ❏
ARUP . . . . ❏
ASDA . . . . ❏
ASTRAZENECA . . . . ❏
ATKINS . . . . ❏
BAE SYSTEMS . . . . ❏
BANK OF AMERICA . . . . ❏
BARCLAYS BANK . . . . ❏
BARCLAYS CAPITAL . . . . ❏
BBC . . . . ❏
BLOOMBERG . . . . ❏
BNP PARIBAS . . . . ❏
BOSTON CONSULTING GROUP. ❏
BP . . . . ❏
BRITISH AIRWAYS . . . . ❏
BT . . . . ❏
CADBURY . . . . ❏
CANCER RESEARCH UK . . . . . ❏
CITI . . . . ❏
CIVIL SERVICE FAST STREAM . . ❏
CLIFFORD CHANCE . . . . ❏
CMS CAMERON MCKENNA . . . ❏
CO-OPERATIVE GROUP . . . . . . ❏
CORUS . . . . ❏
CREDIT SUISSE . . . . ❏
DATA CONNECTION . . . . ❏
DELOITTE . . . . ❏
DEUTSCHE BANK . . . . ❏
DLA PIPER . . . . ❏
E.ON . . . . ❏
ERNST & YOUNG . . . . ❏
EVERSHEDS . . . . ❏
EXXONMOBIL . . . . ❏
FABER MAUNSELL . . . . ❏
FOREIGN OFFICE . . . . ❏
FRESHFIELDS BRUCKHAUS
DERINGER . . . . ❏
FUJITSU . . . . ❏
GCHQ . . . . ❏
GLAXOSMITHKLINE . . . . ❏
GOLDMAN SACHS . . . . ❏
GOOGLE . . . . ❏

GRANT THORNTON . . . . ❏
HBOS . . . . ❏
HERBERT SMITH . . . . ❏
HSBC . . . . ❏
IBM . . . . ❏
JOHN LEWIS . . . . ❏
J.P. MORGAN . . . . ❏
KPMG . . . . ❏
L'ORÉAL . . . . ❏
LINKLATERS . . . . ❏
LLOYDS TSB . . . . ❏
LOVELLS . . . . ❏
MARKS & SPENCER . . . . ❏
MARS . . . . ❏
McDONALD'S RESTAURANTS . . ❏
McKINSEY & COMPANY . . . . . . ❏
MERRILL LYNCH . . . . ❏
MET OFFICE . . . . ❏
METROPOLITAN POLICE . . . . . ❏
MI5 – THE SECURITY SERVICE . ❏
MICROSOFT . . . . ❏
MINISTRY OF DEFENCE . . . . . . ❏
MORGAN STANLEY . . . . ❏
NGDP FOR LOCAL GOVERNMENT . ❏
NHS . . . . ❏
NPOWER . . . . ❏
OXFAM . . . . ❏
PENGUIN . . . . ❏
POLICE HPDS . . . . ❏
PRICEWATERHOUSECOOPERS . ❏
PROCTER & GAMBLE . . . . ❏
QINETIQ . . . . ❏
ROLLS-ROYCE . . . . ❏
ROYAL AIR FORCE . . . . ❏
ROYAL BANK OF SCOTLAND GP . ❏
ROYAL NAVY . . . . ❏
SAINSBURY'S . . . . ❏
SHELL . . . . ❏
SKY . . . . ❏
SLAUGHTER AND MAY . . . . ❏
TEACH FIRST . . . . ❏
TESCO . . . . ❏
THOMSON REUTERS . . . . ❏
TRANSPORT FOR LONDON . . . . ❏
UBS . . . . ❏
UNILEVER . . . . ❏
WATSON WYATT . . . . ❏
WPP . . . . ❏

THE INSTITUTE OF CHARTERED ACCOUNTANTS IN ENGLAND & WALES

THE TIMES
TOP 100
GRADUATE EMPLOYERS

Find out more about Britain's top graduate employers and you could start your career £5,000 richer!

Business Reply
License Number
RRLB-HASE-XAHC

High Fliers Publications Ltd
King's Gate
1 Bravingtons Walk
LONDON
N1 9AE